NURSES:
POWER AND POLITICS

Biographical Note

Trevor Clay has been General Secretary of the RCN since 1982, after 3 years as Deputy General Secretary. He trained at the Coventry Hospitals Group and the Bethlem Royal and Maudsley Hospitals in London. In 1964, he became the first man at Guys Hospital to hold full sister's rank. After posts in Welwyn Garden City and at the Northwest Metropolitan Regional Hospital Board, he went as Director of Nursing to the Whittington Hospital in Highgate, where he was then Chief Nursing Officer. He took a year's sabbatical leave in 1972–73 at Brunel University to study for a Master's degree in Public and Social Administration and then was appointed Area Nursing Officer for Camden and Islington. He is a Fellow of the RCN and a member of the Board of Directors of the International Council of Nurses.

NURSES
Power and Politics

Trevor Clay MPhil, RGN, RMN, FRCN
General Secretary, Royal College of Nursing

In association with
Alison Dunn, *Director of Press and Public Relations RCN*
and Neil Stewart, *Parliamentary Liaison Officer RCN*

Foreword by
Virginia Henderson
Emeritus Professor of Nursing, Yale University

Heinemann Nursing
London

William Heinemann Medical Books
22 Bedford Square
London WC1B 3HH

ISBN 0–433–06005–0

First published 1987
Reprinted 1987

Typeset by Eta Services (Typesetters) Ltd, Beccles, Suffolk
and printed and bound in Great Britain by
Biddles Ltd, Guildford and King's Lynn

Contents

Foreword

Nothing could be more timely than this very interesting and highly informative book. Partly because the World Health Organisation endorses nurses as principal providers of primary care (if the goal of health for all by the year 2000 is to be reached) nurses everywhere are hoping, and many are trying, to create systems enabling them to realise this potential usefulness to society.

Trevor Clay says that *Nurses: Power and Politics* is intended to stimulate debate on the nature of such a system and how it can be developed. While he says he does not expect readers to agree with every opinion he expresses, few will fail to sense that he has had more than a little success in effecting change, and it is hard to escape the conclusion that he is eminently prepared to advise as well as to discuss, or debate, the relationships suggested by the book's title. His formal education includes a graduate degree in management from Brunel University; and he has held a wide range of posts in the NHS. Trevor Clay is now General Secretary of the fastest growing professional trade union in the United Kingdom. And currently, as a Board member of the International Council of Nurses, he has, increasingly, a worldwide viewpoint.

Nurses: Power and Politics focuses on the role of the nurse in the NHS since its establishment in 1948. This involves a discussion of the forces inside and outside the profession that have shaped the role of the nurse; the ethical questions affecting nursing, or 'matters of conscience'; the education of nurses; the nature of their work—their 'real work'; the hierarchies in health service, especially in the nursing ranks; the public and self-image of the nurse; the effect on nursing of its being so largely a woman's profession; the influence of the woman's movement and the role of male nurses; and, particularly in the United Kingdom, the influence of trade unions.

The discussion of all these topics is carefully documented with reference to the reports of investigations and the legislation that have affected nurses and their work. Trevor Clay points out the tendency nurses have had in the past to let others conduct such studies and promote legislation that has sealed their fate—determined their roles. But, he says, he is an optimist and he discusses some recent developments (as for instance the Cumberlege Report on home care and Project 2000 dealing with educational reform, that show nurses being more 'assertive') as trying to influence the conditions under which they work and, in fact, living conditions for all citizens.

Even though the discussion is focused on the United Kingdom there are references throughout to related developments in other countries, and published sources of information are not confined to British books and journals.

In the style adopted by Trevor Clay he can speak to all literate persons—those inside and outside health services, providers and consumers alike. In an age when we stress 'self-help' and participation of the public in planning health programmes, it is fortunate that this instructive book can be read with interest and profit by any one interested in promoting health services. While it is obviously a scholarly work none of the barriers of pretentious language or jargon have been used that limit the accessibility of so much that is written by health care professionals. The author shows by his stress on communication within nursing organisations and the ability of nurses to speak with one voice (or to take concerted action) that he sees communication as a priority. This is no cook book but neither is it a theoretical discourse. A number of chapters include a list of practical points to consider or steps to take that will enable nurses to reach certain goals.

This is a model publication for nurses everywhere who are trying to create a health care system in which they can work more effectively. *Nurses: Power and Politics* suggests to the most casual reader that knowledge generates power. The concluding chapter ends with the statement, 'Participation in the political life of the country is the alternative for individual nurses to the silent frustration of the past or industrial action (striking, etc.).' Nurses are urged to 'look beyond' the immediate frustration of not being able to give all they would wish for today's patients and to do all in their power through nursing organisations to 'be sure that tomorrow's people get the nurses and nursing they deserve'.

Virginia Henderson RN, MA

Acknowledgements

I am deeply grateful for the help and inspiration provided by so many of my colleagues at the RCN, and in the profession generally in talking through ideas and drafts. I am especially grateful to Lindsay Collett, Nikki Cartwright and Michele Millard who typed so many of the drafts in their own time; my warm thanks are also due to Alison Bramley and the staff of the RCN Library who provided source and background material.

Finally, this book could not have been written without the enormous hard work and commitment of my colleagues, Alison Dunn and Neil Stewart, who have been my assistants on this project and who are as committed to the nursing profession and to the Royal College of Nursing as anyone I have ever known.

Preface

This is a personal book. It is not the official manifesto of the Royal College of Nursing—that was published in a pamphlet in September 1986. As I have been a member of the RCN for 25 years and General Secretary for 5 of those, I have written a book primarily about the College and its aims and ambitions, which chronicles some of its hopes and disappointments as well as signals battles which it will go on fighting.

On the day she retired my predecessor, Dame Catherine Hall said 'You may not necessarily accept it now but you will find being General Secretary of the College to be a way of life—you won't be able to separate the personal year from the General Secretary year'. She was right. The RCN is now the largest nurses' organisation in the world. It has nearly 500 staff in 22 locations in the UK and nearly 260,000 members. The fight for better salaries and education for nurses has been going on for most of this century; certainly for the past 50 years. The fight is intensifying now that the profession is able to display more unity and has accepted that politics and power are not necessarily dirty words but important routes which have to be followed for success. Nurses are also some of the most responsible people in society because of the very nature of their work. In my view society would do well to watch the chemistry of politics and power and the responsibility very carefully indeed. That is fundamentally what this book is about.

DEDICATION

This book is dedicated to all those nurses
who fought so many battles for the
profession, and to those who will.

CHAPTER 1

Introduction

Nursing, power and politics are not words that usually go together. The public, and nurses themselves, see nursing as outside politics and political power struggles. That view is reinforced in the literature of nursing—in Britain at least—where polemical works about the organisation of nursing in relation to the rest of society are thin on the ground. Nursing is a remarkably insular profession, which has taken little heed of the great social, political and economic forces that have shaped and surrounded its practice.

So much of the work of nurses is about coping, about getting through the day, about giving of yourself to someone else. We are sometimes guilty of not taking time to lift our heads from the bedside to look at what is happening around us. I have spent my working life in nursing and nursing politics, and have become increasingly convinced that one of the greatest strengths of nurses and nursing—concentration on the personal and individual needs of the patient—is also one of our greatest weaknesses. We are required to deny our own feelings and needs to create confidence and calm in others. Too many nurses take that suppression of their individual feelings on a daily basis into political life. Nursing is perhaps the most unassertive profession in the UK, yet more than ever, we need collectively to look beyond immediate problems and preoccupations to see the forces that are active around us and to tackle them.

The illusion that nursing is outside the battle for resources must surely be over for most nurses. The immense struggle to get the 1979 Nurses, Midwives and Health Visitors Act on the statute book to establish the United Kingdom Central Council for Nursing, Midwifery and Health Visiting acutely highlighted this for me. The NHS pay dispute in 1982, and the Griffiths general management reorganisation with its huge impact on the independence of nursing within the health service, confirmed it. The struggle over the reform of nurse education combined with public debate over the government's Green Paper on primary health care and the Cumberlege Report on community nursing emphasised it. No one can be in any doubt that nursing's future is being decided in the public domain, and that nurses, both individually and through their organisations, must participate fully in that debate.

The isolation and non-participation of nurses in the policy argument which affects the future of their practice and the services they can give is compounded by the fact that 90 per cent of nurses are women, many of whom have children and other family commitments, with all the social and cultural obstacles to active participation in political life this brings.

That the personal is political is one of the main messages of the women's movement. Jane Salvage, in her book *The Politics of Nursing* (1985), argues that nurses must confront the consequences of political and policy decisions as they affect them in work and in their personal experience of those decisions at the bedside. On one level I agree with her. Nurses need to recognise that many of the daily dilemmas and choices they face are imposed on them because of broader decisions taken elsewhere. Their response cannot be left to other people. On the other hand I can see among the nurses I represent a genuine reluctance to introduce conflict into the environment because they feel it might alter the special relationship they have with patients. They see their prime task locally, in the wards and in people's homes, as to create calm, reassurance, confidence and trust in a way that contributes to the recovery and happiness of someone at their most vulnerable.

When we say that the personal is political, we look to individual nurses to begin to tackle the political at the personal level. But we must be discriminating. I support nurses who challenge the hierarchy, doctors or general managers, when they feel they have to. A little personal confrontation can be more constructive than passive acceptance. Yet we must protect the patient and avoid placing him or her in the no-man's land between the trenches. The patient is in no position to tackle the problem, being unable to join the conflict. This, of course, is the traditional dilemma facing nursing, and nurses have felt the full force of this blackmail. The nurse's understandable reluctance to confront problems in case they impinge on patients has been used against nurses by nurse managers, other professions and the government. The sense of guilt at risking political activity locally has infected nursing at all levels.

But there is another way. Nurses must be able to fight for the changes they want without turning the ward into a battle-ground. The route lies through organising as a profession and as a trade union, by recognising that the public control of the national health service gives us the opportunity to bring public pressure on government and employers alike.

It is one of the great contradictions of nursing that while nurses every day face suffering, drama, trauma and misery and cope with it, they find political participation difficult and frightening. Nurses who work in accident and emergency departments, coping with all kinds of people who come in off the streets, suddenly go weak at the knees when they have to speak in public or meet a politician. Nurses who have to talk constantly to distraught relatives, calming them and persuading them to take sensible courses of action, lack confidence when asked to assert the needs of their profession in public. This stems not from the nature of their work but from years of socialisation within nursing itself which we now urgently need to break for the good of the profession.

I have made no secret of my objective: bring nurses and nursing more openly into politics. It is only by fighting and winning battles over resources, organisation and policy in the public arena that we can avoid those conflicts intruding into the private and personal relationships that individual nurses must have with the people they serve.

I do not share the view that because governments are guilty of creating problems in the NHS through lack of resources we are justified in introducing further conflict at that level. That is the false conclusion of 'the personal is political'. At its simplest, two wrongs do not make right. But to do nothing is also wrong, and nurses have a right to look to the RCN to chart ways in which they can influence their working environment and control the service they are able to give to their patients without conflict impinging on the patients. This is not an impossible objective or naive expectation. It is the expressed view of the majority of nurses every time they reject the use of industrial action to pursue their grievances. They want an alternative. Having expressed that view consistently over the past decade when the question of nurses taking industrial action has arisen, I have drawn the firm conclusion that the RCN must gear itself to winning change by other means.

Industrial action has the advantage that each person can see exactly what is required of him or her at a particular moment. Participation in wider political activity requires an overview of the economic and social situation in nursing, of the forces inside and outside nursing which will affect it, and of the organisational possibilities. This is the overview which I have been required to take since becoming General Secretary in July 1982. This is the overview which all my predecessors have had to take. But no-one before now has put it down on paper.

It is impossible to satisfy everyone. One view expressed among conservative supporters is that the RCN and nursing are on the slippery slope to an industrial model of trade unionism, and that before long we will begin to put our members' interests above those of our patients and take industrial action. The entry into the political arena is seen in this light and opposed. Some labour and trade union supporters say that the RCN is on the road to full-blown trade unionism in the traditional sense, and that this is no bad thing. At the other end of the spectrum is the view that because the RCN refuses to take industrial action, it is forever in the pocket of the government and the establishment, and has denied itself the only weapon that will make any difference to this or any government. None of these simplistic characterisations are accurate or reflect a careful examination of what the RCN has been doing over the past few years. We have developed a power base for nursing outside industrial action, and I hope to indicate how and why that has been done.

This book is deliberately aimed at creating a debate. It would be wrong of me to go on encouraging nurses to become involved in the wider political process without setting out what I believe to be the basic approach we should take, and how we should tackle some of the major issues we face in the short and medium term. I am sceptical that there is such a thing as the long term in politics. Nurses sometimes feel uncomfortable with the political process because long-term certainties are few, while short-term risks abound. Nurses are not risk takers in their work and that translates directly into their political participation. In mapping out what the choices and difficulties are, I hope that I will be able to improve the confidence and sense of certainty which so many nurses want before entering into such an insecure public arena to argue their case.

In looking at the political environment, I want to draw attention to the many powerful forces that are working on the nursing service and the NHS. I am deeply committed to the NHS as a method of organising the delivery of health care. I believe that society should take collective responsibility for the health of all its people and that the test of a truly civilised society is that health care should be free at the point of delivery and available where the need exists. I welcome the increasing emphasis on individuals taking responsibility for their own health, but I reject the idea that this should be taken as far as to say that when they fall ill it is their own fault and the solution must lie in their own hands. It cannot, for that is the moment when they are most vulnerable and dependent.

Nursing has to work within the health-care framework that surrounds our practice. Our first priority must be to try to guarantee the best system of general health care for all the people, and I have no doubt that this lies within the framework of the National Health Service. The financial and organisational health of that service is the main factor affecting the well-being of nursing and the service we are able to give. We must look at ways in which we can promote the development of the health service and contribute to ideas about new directions it might take to promote health and prevent illness, rather than simply acting as the band aid for society and all its ills. I want to give some indications of how I think that might be achieved.

Every nurse is now aware that the public purse is limited and that resources for meeting health care needs are being constrained—a worldwide problem. This is likely to continue under any government. The question remains how the cake is to be divided, and the priority within the public purse that is to be given to health and to nursing within the NHS. Such arguments inevitably involve a debate which means questioning other political priorities of the government of the day. It is a debate which can no longer be avoided by nurses and the question therefore is how best and most effectively to participate.

The Griffiths Report (DHSS 1983) came as a profound shock to nurse leaders, undermining the independence of the nursing profession and its control over the practice of nursing. The introduction of general management is the most obvious example of nursing being taken by surprise by outside forces which have been building up in society for many years. The roots of general management can be traced to the late 1970s and the disillusionment felt among politicians of all parties with the failure of the 1974 reorganisation. With the benefit of hindsight we can see that the concept of general management and accountability, which was so far advanced in the private sector of industry and commerce, would eventually impinge on the public sector. Of course it should not have been a surprise. The concept of general management in the public sector was not peculiar to the NHS and had been a preoccupation of the Conservatives from the moment they came into office in 1979. The idea was firmed up in the *Financial Management Initiative* (Treasury 1983), launched across several government departments, whose implementation began in earnest after the 1983 general election. The effect in nursing was traumatic, not just for those who lost their jobs or had to apply for a hybrid post, but because it came at a time when nursing was preparing itself for the reform of nursing education and engaged in the debate about community nursing set off by the Cumberlege Report.

A changing philosophy in industry, commerce and government came to have a profound effect on nursing, making the task of internal reform more difficult and placing more obstacles in its way—not for the first time in nursing's history. An important lesson about the need for an overview in nursing was learned. I want to examine a whole range of changes in society and in politics which affect the options available to nursing in the future. We need to be aware of these to plan our course.

Ninety per cent of nurses in this country are women, and the policies we put forward in the health service and the organisational choices we must make as a union must reflect that.

Society is changing its view about how the individual is treated by the state and by professions. The power of professions to sit in judgment on their own codes of practice is being challenged. Patients are demanding a greater regard for their individual dignity, for their privacy, and ultimately for a greater choice over the treatment they receive.

The ethical questions are becoming more complex. I believe that the dilemmas facing nurses every day are undervalued, often misunderstood and usually neglected in favour of a medical-led debate. I will try to set out some of the issues facing nurses in the belief first, that they have not been stated widely enough, and second, that public understanding and awareness is the essential starting point.

The future of nursing practice is not entirely in the hands of nurses. We have to adapt to meet the changing demands and expectations of society. In facing the changing demands and expectations one of the most optimistic signs in recent years has been the debate over the reform of nurse education. As part of this debate the United Kingdom Central Council for Nursing, Midwifery and Health Visiting (UKCC) started its Project 2000 enquiry by examining not what nurses wanted but the changes in society to which nursing would have to respond. The chapters in the UKCC report, *Project 2000*, 'The current context and the case for change', and 'A changing world' represent an important recognition by leaders of nursing that outside forces will have a significant influence on the future. Whether or not this has been recognised in the debate on change where the old, narrow, sectional interests have been evident can only be judged by the outcome of the UKCC's deliberations and recommendations.

Changes are taking place in ideas about trade union organisation and professional representation. The RCN is seen as something of an odd man out, adhering to neither of the two tests of British trade unionism—a willingness to use the strike weapon and membership of the Trades Union Congress. The RCN has an independent stance which comes from the needs of its members and the problems they face, and not from some predetermined political position. Labels such as 'moderate' which are attached to the RCN are an irrelevant shorthand. Hardly any other union or professional organisation has gone to the 'extreme' of taking full-page advertisements in national newspapers to advance its case. We do things differently and I hope the public and nurses will better understand why when they have read this book.

Politics, power and nursing are part of the same fabric. The profession cannot separate them and I do not intend to do so in this book. It would be an inadequate overview which did not address the major current issues inside nursing. General management has accelerated a debate about the structure and hierarchy of nursing. A clinical career structure is back on the agenda and we need to think clearly about exactly what we mean and what a clinical career structure should reward. I will look at nursing education and the changes in prospect, and the tensions the debate has created both with the government and within the profession itself.

The UKCC's own *Code of Professional Practice* has provoked discussion about the responsibilities of the nurse in relation to the environment of care, forcing nurses out into wider debates about the funding and running of the health service. This is welcome, but the implications need to be more widely aired.

What should nurses do about the opportunity for an extended role which is presented in the Green Paper on primary health care and in the Cumberlege Report on Community Nursing? Do we have a duty to argue for an extended role or are we simply indulging, as many imagine, in professional vanity? I hope to show that extending the role of nursing is about a great deal more than chasing after the medical model of care. There is a gap in future care which only nursing can fill.

Nursing itself has internal divisions about future directions, and nowhere are they stronger than in the debate over the future of the enrolled nurse grade. The present Conservative government and the trade unions have come together in a remarkable alliance in defence of enrolled nurse training, but for entirely different reasons. A second grade of nurse has long been held up as the solution to all the NHS's manpower problems. Yet we have had the enrolled nurse for over 40 years and still the manpower problems recur. It clearly is not a solution. So why do government, some unions and some nurse managers cling so strongly to this grading of nurse?

The nursing profession itself is not united. I recall with some horror and concern for the current attempts to reform nurse education, the divisions which occurred over the passing of the 1979 Nurses, Midwives and Health Visitors Act. As the clock ticked away toward the 1979 election and the collapse of the legislation the different nurses' organisations squabbled among themselves. Sectional interest was everything. The clear warning that the new government might have nothing to do with reforming nurse education was disregarded. Such short-sightedness in the face of the most obvious political timetable was staggering. Are we in danger of repeating it over nurse education?

The Labour Health Minister, Roland Moyle, and the nursing

division of the DHSS must take much of the credit for steering that legislation through despite divisions. The legislation and the statutory bodies it established, however, still reflect many of those divisions. National divisions are still there, and while the existence of an English National Board as well as a United Kingdom Central Council may look well on paper, in practice it has produced much conflict and unnecessary competition for the ear of government. Even the title of the statutory body—The United Kingdom Central Council for Nursing, Midwifery and Health Visiting—reflects the fighting that went on that year.

Then in 1986, in the middle of the debate about the future of nursing education, the President of the Royal College of Midwives, Joyce Beak, told their annual conference that midwifery is not a branch of nursing, as proposed in the UKCC Project 2000 paper, but a separate tree. If nursing is not careful it will not be outside forces which defeat our desire for change, but, once again, divisions within nursing.

Despite all these problems, nursing, and the RCN in particular, is stronger than ever. The membership figures for the RCN show a growth of over 100 per cent since the late 1970s. Each new member means one more nurse coming out of her shell and making a contribution to the voice of nursing in the national political debate. Despite the adversity in which most unions and professional membership organisations have found themselves, nursing has, over the seven years from 1979 to 1986, seen the numbers of nurses increase dramatically and the RCN become the fastest growing trade union during that period. We enjoy a high level of public support and confidence and have had little of the damaging publicity suffered by other professions whose commitment to the public has been consistently questioned in the courts and the media since the mid-seventies.

Members join trade unions and professional organisations for a variety of reasons. Invariably it involves some deviation from the norm of activity. They join to have us deal with the crises in their working and professional lives. Reasons might be personal and individual. People may need representation when their employment is under threat, when they are being disciplined, or when they are being sued for negligence. More likely it is when they are being affected collectively by government or management change. Someone has to negotiate on their behalf. They may want someone to press positively to make sure their reward for work and commitment is recognised in pay and conditions or they may wish positively to change policy and advance the science and art of nursing.

As an organisation the function of which is to deal with crisis and change on behalf of thousands of members, the RCN has to face all the pressures that crisis and change bring and seek to manage them as constructively as possible for the good of the members and the public, and for the advancement of the science and art of nursing. The ideal is that these three objectives should always be in step. Unfortunately that is not always the case. All the contradictions and conflicts in nursing are evident in an organisation like the RCN and the issues it confronts. Often a member will question a policy. She may be looking locally and in the short term, where the Council are taking more cognisance of outside forces and adapting to meet them. In short, like all general secretaries I find that the world outside and the motives of the RCN look very different to members than they do from my own position. I hope that by the time the reader has finished this book he or she will have a better understanding of the choices that have to be made and the forces in play, even if they do not agree with my conclusions.

I hope to bring the strands together and indicate where I think we should go in the short and medium terms, what essential objectives nursing should maintain, and what tactics we should adopt to promote our profession and advance the interests of our members.

I have received two sets of advice about writing this book. The first is that it is the duty of someone holding the office of general secretary of the RCN to set out their views and calculations as openly and bluntly as possible; that I should start a debate in nursing to give nurses a better chance of understanding the overview of events; and that despite the conflict the debate may generate, it will contribute to the growing political maturity of nurses and nursing. The alternative view is that a narrow section in nursing is not yet ready for this debate and that many who represent it hold senior positions in nursing. Many achieved their position without the intrusion of political debate and without regard to their ability to cope with wider political issues. They will feel threatened and insecure and will attack the messenger who brings the news that it is time for nursing to come out of its shell before the outside world tears it out. I have opted to publish. Bow-ing to the second view is not an option. Events and time will not stand still, change is coming and the better we understand it the better we can cope and make sure it is on our terms. I hope this book contributes something to a greater understanding of the challenges and the way ahead.

References

Department of Health and Social Security (1983) *NHS Management Inquiry Report* (Griffiths Report). London: HMSO.

Department of Health and Social Security (1984) HC(84)13 *Health Services Management Implementation in the NHS*. Management Inquiry Report. London: HMSO.

Department of Health and Social Security (1986) *Neighbourhood Nursing: A Focus for Care* (Cumberlege Report). The Community Nursing Review. London: HMSO.

Department of Health and Social Security (1986) *Primary Health Care: An Agenda for Discussion*. London: HMSO.

Salvage, J. (1985) *The Politics of Nursing*. London: Heinemann Nursing.

Treasury (1983) *Financial Management Initiative: Financial management in government departments*. London: HMSO.

United Kingdom Central Council for Nursing, Midwifery and Health Visiting (1984) *Code of Professional Conduct*. London: UKCC.

United Kingdom Central Council for Nursing, Midwifery and Health Visiting (1986) *Project 2000: A new preparation for practice*. London: UKCC.

CHAPTER 2

Outside forces

It is hard to imagine a more fundamental change in the way in which health care is delivered than the establishment of the NHS in 1948. Yet that apparently revolutionary change had its own form of conservativism, which is only now beginning to be challenged from outside the world of health care professionals. The pressures for change provide nursing with both dangers and opportunities.

The decision to provide health care in the UK within a state system funded from taxation and free at the point of delivery represented a fundamental change, but in the fight to achieve it much else remained unchanged. The new NHS inherited the old hospitals and the old working patterns of doctors and nurses. Despite good intentions about bringing change, and giving priority to preventing illness and promoting health, the NHS remained primarily a sickness service. It delivered what care and treatment it could on a model dictated by the medical profession and the administrative arrangements which they had dominated in the hospitals and public health services before nationalisation.

While the administrative and economic base of health delivery changed, very few other radical questions were asked. Many thought they were not necessary. In 1948, there was every reason to be optimistic about the future. Britain, one of the five wealthiest countries in the world, with a substantial empire behind it, ought to be able to afford whatever health care it desired. Relative economic prosperity enabled the new NHS to carry on and expand the practices and divisions of duties it had inherited.

The second reason for neglect of the basic economic dimensions in health was the naive belief that as the health service became more effective in preventing illness, so the economic demands of ill health would decline.

This is the first external factor which now bears heavily on the modern health service. Prevention is not cheaper. While the proper objective for a health service is the promotion and maintenance of health, for the health economist the key question is how people will die, or rather how long they will live. It is in denying death that the greatest costs are incurred. The irony is that successful health promotion, while giving many more years of activity, creates an elderly, frail population who need good expensive care rather than dramatic cure.

Between 1948 and the mid-1970s, the health service embarked on a dramatic expansion of services. It was possible in the 1960s to step into a new hospital and recognise all the old relationships perpetuated. In some cases, they had become even more entrenched in a service which had no particular reason to ask itself questions about how services could be made more effective.

The health service, and nursing within it, enjoyed a long period of consensus about how it should be run and expanded. None of the major parties questioned the fundamental financial and administrative relationships between the state and the providers of health care. This was a period in which the politicians gave much ground to the health professionals in determining the direction the service should take and how it should be run. The economic crisis of the mid-1970s destroyed that cosy relationship and forced a fundamental re-examination of patterns and priorities. The Royal Commission on the NHS (1979) observed, 'The NHS could not shelter from the country's chill economic climate in the mid-1970s'.

The economic pressures both combined with and generated powerful criticism of the delivery of health care. On the economic problems, the focus moved to other countries. International comparisons with the USA or Scandinavian countries increasingly led politicans to the conclusion that if we could start again we would not start from here.

The political consensus was broken by the Conservative Party, whose libertarian wing in particular began to ask questions about the role of the state in health care and to draw their own conclusions from international comparisons. The new Conservatives unleashed a general critique of the professions which inevitably included questions about the medical profession and its role in health service policy making.

The critical climate was reinforced by the awakening women's movement, which found the health service male-dominated and 'uncaring' in its attitudes and priorities. They added to the challenge being presented to the medical profession. The 1970s saw the beginning of a consumer response which may have begun with concern about cars and washing machines but ultimately touched the health and social services. It led to the creation of Community Health Councils and to the growing confidence of individuals that they could question health policy and priorities and challenge the doctors about the degree of choice in treatment and care.

The Labour Party and the trade unions, who had been the greatest allies of the health service, seeing it as the single greatest socialist achievement of the post-war years, were becoming increasingly disillusioned as their brainchild grew older. Like other parts of the public bureaucracy, it seemed to have a life of its own. Health administrators and professionals alike joined groups, like civil servants, in the demonology of those who held up progress.

The unions suffered the disillusionment of dealing with a public employer they found hard to distinguish from private sector employers. After years of pay restraint and a freeze on the growth of health budgets in the late 1970s, much of this frustration boiled over in the Winter of Discontent in 1979.

The elderly, the mentally ill and the mentally handicapped were finally publicly noticed in the mid-1970s and the standards of care they received were questioned. Was it really appropriate and cost-effective to keep people in the institutional environment of hospitals? The answer was clearly no, and the seeds of the policy of wholesale 'care in the community' were sown—the full implications of which we are realising only now.

Economic Pressures

The optimism and the economic growth of the postwar years provided not only increased resources but a bigger slice of a larger cake. In 1949, the NHS consumed £414 million, which represented 3.95 per cent of GDP. By 1982, the NHS was spending £10,856 million which represented 6.2 per cent of GDP. Since 1982, that percentage of GDP has remained static and may actually have dropped slightly. The first wave of economic constraint to hit the NHS was the cuts in capital monies following the IMF loan to the Labour Government of 1976; the second was the increase in oil prices in 1979. This was coupled with the election of a Conservative government who immediately sought to cut the proportion of the nation's wealth which went on public expenditure and confirmed that the pursuit of restraint would be continued.

First, a tier of health-service management was abolished in 1982 in an attempt to save money and streamline the service. In 1983 'competitive tendering' was designed to stem the growth in costs, particularly in domestic and catering services. Then came the implementation of general management following the verdict of the Griffiths enquiry. 1984–85 saw the pursuit of 'efficiency savings' which the government were convinced could be made in the service.

These are all signs of government attempts to come to terms with the end of economic prosperity and guaranteed growth which would allow the amount of money spent on the health service to increase beyond the growth in the economy generally. We have reached a plateau of public expenditure, and government are exhausting, one by one, all the options available to constrain and cut resources. Capital cuts, administrative reductions, new management arrangements, and new market disciplines imposed on ancillary staffs, bring the government closer, step by step, to the question of the use of the major resource in the health service, the people who work in it, and their skills. The division of labour is a question that ministers would probably prefer to avoid publicly, since it risks bringing them into conflict with the medical profession and, perhaps, even the nursing profession.

This conflict could perhaps be postponed if the problem was one of keeping the health service ticking over in an unchanging world. But the world is changing. New policies emphasising health promotion and prevention are needed. The population grows older, bringing new kinds of demands for health care which the hospital-dominated medical model finds hard—and expensive—to cope with.

This dilemma is similar to the problems faced by developing countries in providing low-cost basic care for expanding populations. They are asking basic questions about the level of skill required to provide the best health care most cost-effectively. Many different names, such as 'barefoot doctor', are used but the basic skills are those we would associate generally with nursing. It took several decades for the World Health Organisation openly to recognise nurses as the key to primary health care. The declaration of Alma Ata and of 'Health for All by the Year 2000' marked the beginning of the change.

The NHS is no longer growing fast enough to keep up with either the growing numbers of elderly people or the increasing costs of medical technology, let alone meet the demands made on the service by new technological and medical procedures or diseases such as AIDS. Anxiety about the growing costs of health care is not peculiar to the United Kingdom. In almost all developed industrial economies, the rise in the cost of health care is being challenged. In particular, in the USA under a largely insurance-based system, the government have become so concerned at the explosion in health care costs that they have initiated measures to contain them both in hospitals and in the community. The imposition of the Health Maintenance Organisation (HMO) and the introduction of Diagnostic Related Groups (DRGs) are essentially an attempt by the US government to control health-care costs in the public sector.

Looking to the economic future, none of the political parties in the United Kingdom are promising large increase in NHS expenditure. The redistribution of resources will have to continue. The Conservative government has only just begun to address these questions in its latest Green Paper on Primary Health Care (1986). The key question for the NHS is asked: 'Are we realising the full potential of nurses?' In my view, the answer is clearly 'no', for both professional and economic reasons. I do not want nurses simply to fill the gaps left by doctors but to take over areas of care which are presently neglected and of which they will be the best providers.

International Pressures

New ideas and new examples of how health care can be provided more effectively are now arriving from abroad. From the USA, there comes the notion of the nurse practitioner trained to a high level of competence and working more independently of the doctors in the community and in hospitals. Many would recognise much of the nurse practitioner's work as being within the competence of a district nurse or health visitor. But in this country we still work under the convention that nurses do not have patients. All patients 'belong' to a doctor who is responsible for their treatment and care.

We no longer lead the world in the way we educate and train our nurses and this reflects on the standard of care that is given. This has been a problem in the United Kingdom since the Second World War, as we show in Chapter 6. There have been a series of reports, from both government and the nursing profession, which confirm this. In each case, either the nursing profession or the government saw proposals for change as a dangerous step in the dark without guaranteed results. But while the UK dithered, change into higher education went ahead; in Canada, Australia, New Zealand and Israel. The experience of these countries is now a powerful weapon in the armoury of nursing in the United Kingdom in its fight for educational reform.

International pressures exert themselves in other ways. The UK government is committed, as a member of WHO, to its strategy of Health for All by the Year 2000 and has accepted the need to meet the objectives set down in that strategy for the development of new primary health care services. This philosophy has begun to have an effect on the debate in the UK about priorities in health care. As part of the European Community, the UK has had to comply in its nurse training with the painfully negotiated Directives to facilitate freedom of movement for nurses in the European Community. Few have taken advantage of this, but the freedom of movement of ideas and standards has grown apace. It is no longer easy to claim that Britain's health service is the best in the world.

Political Pressure

It is difficult to believe today that a consensus about the delivery of health care existed among all the political parties from the end of the Second World War until the mid-1970s. The economic crisis precipitated by the rise in oil prices in 1974 both sharpened attitudes and divided the political parties. The election of Mrs Thatcher to the leadership of the Conservative Party in 1975 heralded widespread criticism of the state and the public sector which included an attack on the near monopoly held by the NHS. Sir Keith Joseph quickly became disappointed by the reorganisation of the health service which he had overseen as

Secretary of State in the Heath Government. This coincided with the final attempt by Barbara Castle, who replaced him after Labour won the 1974 General Elections, to abolish all pay beds from the NHS, an issue which was to polarise the debate about state and private health provision. It raised issues of freedom of choice, highlighting the cracks in the health service itself and giving a sudden added impetus to the alternative: private health care.

Things were not calm among the supporters of the NHS in the Labour Party, which was becoming hostile to the size of the bureaucracy it had created. As the government, it received public criticism for the NHS's slow response to public need and its poor image with members of the public. Other parts of the public and civil service bore the brunt of such discontent about how services should be run, but the NHS did not escape criticism.

The reorganisation of 1974 was seen in the Labour Party as removing the final parts of the health service from democratic local control. This issue has stayed alive to this day and is now reflected in the fact that all the opposition parties will be going into the next election with promises to restore some degree of local control or influence over the health service. The demonology which was being built up in the Labour movement about the interests and motives of civil servants was applied by many to the senior officers involved in running the health service.

Labour in government was just as concerned about the runaway costs of health care and the lack of effective counter-action as the service was. David Ennals, the Secretary of State for Social Services until the end of the Callaghan Government, had to bear the frustration of closing 272 hospitals during his time in office and then losing office before he had experienced any public gratitude for the many new hospitals he commissioned. Politicians of all parties were losing patience with the health service for very different reasons.

Disillusionment

Among the supporters of the health service, none had been stronger than the TUC-affiliated public service unions, yet for them the experience of the late 1970s was a bitter one. By 1979 many of their members felt little personal loyalty to the service or willingness to defend it in public. They had been on the receiving end of several reorganisations. From 1976 onwards, they had been subject to various forms of pay restraint. Their absolute pay was low, and in a period of high inflation they saw their relative position being dramatically eroded. The management of the health service seemed no different in style from that of many private companies; a complaint which unions and sections of the Left were making about all nationalised industries.

The Winter of Discontent in 1978–79 saw this trouble boil over into industrial action, with a public reaction that carried over into the 1979 election. Any status which might have derived from working in the health service was severely undermined, in the minds both of the public and of those working for the health service.

Disillusionment was widespread. Later it was reflected in the boom in private health insurance and in the fratricidal debates which took place among unions about whether such insurance had any role to play in the packages they negotiated for their members. The consensus was broken not just between the parties but within them as well.

The 1982 pay dispute ran for much longer than the industrial action of 1979 and those involved learned from previous troubles, concentrating much more on arguing about the general state of the health service. By 1983, the Conservative government had brought new external factors to bear on ancillary services with the introduction of 'competitive tendering'. The experience for many of those working in the health service has continued to be one of bitterness and disillusionment.

Consumers of the Service

Of all the people who use the health service, the most powerful consumer critique has come from women. This is not surprising since they are its greatest users. Consumer power has risen to challenge the decision-making processes, particularly of the doctors. As health authorities began to pursue change and redistribution of services and the closure of older hospitals, they came up against fierce opposition from both local groups and trade unions. The pressure for greater consultation on any local changes grew throughout the 1970s. From the user's point of view, the health service remains geared to the needs and demands of those who run it rather than those who use it. Visiting times, the doctor's round, outpatient departments' appointment systems, the waiting times, and the ambulance services were all perceived to be guilty, as was nursing, of organising care with too much concentration on their own convenience. The private sector found a powerful weapon to attract new custom in this area.

In the treatment of women some of the most fundamental questions have been raised about priorities and choices, particularly in abortion, maternity care, contraception, and screening for breast and cervical cancer. In these areas, doctors have been criticised for their approach and reluctance to offer 'choices'. Insensitive and inappropriate forms of treatment, poor advice, and counselling influenced by social prejudice are a few of the accusations which the women's movement has directed at those providing the treatment, and sometimes the care! The credibility and competence of doctors is under attack from politicians and the public. The Wendy Savage case in 1986, in which parts of the medical profession were divided over the use of intervention in deliveries, and from which the consultant Mrs Savage emerged vindicated as an advocate of a woman's right to choose the type of birth, has left a negative impression in the public mind from which the medical profession will have to work hard to recover.

The restrictions on resources for health have also brought the consumers, often through the Community Health Councils, increasingly into conflict with the hospital- and medical-dominated policy makers. The dilemmas described at national level about priorities have their parallel at local level in debates about acquiring new technology for medicine as opposed to spending it on prevention and health screening.

The drug industry and the role of the medical profession in it also underwent a profound crisis in confidence when the full horror of the thalidomide scandal was revealed in the 1970s. The courts, too, had their role to play in breaking down the image of infallability in the NHS as claims for damages increasingly came before them.

The establishment of the health service Ombudsman in 1977 was a landmark. His reports have focused on issues of individual treatment in the NHS, forcing policy changes and greater public accountability.

Medicine has played its own role in changing the perception of what priorities should be adopted. Voices have come not only from outside the professions but also from within, and as medicine has divided between the BMA and the medical Royal Colleges so it has been less able to resist the pressures from consumers and politicians for change.

Population Changes/Manpower Problems

Changes are taking place at the two ends of the population spectrum. In the demand for care, the growing number of elderly people, especially those over the age of 75, which is estimated to grow by almost 100,000 between 1986 and 1996, is central. More importantly for the health service, the numbers over 85, where the dependency rises significantly is estimated to rise by over 120,000 between 1986 and 1996. At present in NHS hospitals, almost 46 per cent of the acute beds are occupied by people over the age of 60. Questions must be asked about how this demand for care is to be met and which are the most appropriate services and professions to meet it.

The second population change which will have a profound effect on how health care is provided is the sharp decline in the number of 18-year-olds from which nursing recruits. In 1966, there were 252,211 nursing staff working in the NHS. By 1977, that figure had risen to 379,699 and in 1986 the total was 485,000. In 20 years, the nursing staff had almost doubled in number. As the number of school leavers was increasing, nursing was able to rely throughout that 20-year period on an increasing number of qualified young people, women in particular, leaving schools with five or more 'O'levels.

Nursing is heavily dependent on this constant flow of recruits because it is dominated by women. The wastage for domestic reasons, and particularly for childbirth, is very high. The point was reached in 1984 where nursing was taking 25 per cent of all the young women school leavers with between five 'O'levels and two 'A'levels.

In research especially undertaken for the RCN Commission for Nursing Education (Judge 1985), it was found that by the early 1990s the drop in the number of suitably qualified young women school leavers with over five 'O'levels would be so great that nursing would need to take 50 per cent of that cohort just to maintain its current numbers. This target is clearly impossible, a shortage is imminent, and will be even more acute if changes in nursing education are not made urgently.

Nursing has had the benefit of a constant flow of young

women coming out of schools in increasing numbers for the past 20 years. With the added pressure of unemployment among young people, nursing has been able to avoid questions about the structure of its workforce and the way it treated its recruits, especially as the vast majority (90 per cent) are women. The wastage in training, which reached 35 per cent in the early 1980s, was ignored because of the constant supply. The rate at which young qualified nurses were leaving because of work, emotional pressures, or the lack of childcare facilities could be ignored while the supply of recruits continued. That situation no longer exists. In the absence of a guaranteed supply key issues must be addressed. First, how can the wastage in nurse education and training be stopped? How can more women be persuaded to remain in the profession for longer or return to it after having a family? The answers to these questions lie in the reform of nursing education and in changing the use of nurses in the health service.

There is another alternative, which is to go for a dilution of the service and to recruit more untrained staff. The scope even for this is very limited compared to the mid-1950s and 1960s when similar dilemmas were faced. There would be problems connected with standards of care as the numbers of trained and untrained staff are already at an unacceptable level. In December 1985, the Department of Health and Social Security, in evidence to the Public Accounts Committee, indicated that of the total of 485,000 (WTE) nursing staff, only 56 per cent were qualified, 20 per cent were in training and the remaining 24 per cent were unqualified auxiliaries and assistants.

The recent dramatic increase in the number of patients being treated has been largely achieved by reducing the time they spend in hospital and massively increasing the number of day cases. As a result, the time they spend in hospital is the short period when they are most dependent on skilled care pre- and post-operatively. The flexibility which used to exist in the 1950s and 1960s for periods of preparation and recuperation no longer obtain. A government which opted for using less trained staff would soon find itself being accused of lowering standards, taking the service over the edge into danger. The price of success in treating more patients in the 1980s is the need for more qualified nursing staff.

All these outside pressures combine to create the conditions for major change in nursing over the coming years. For over 40 years, the RCN has been fighting to move nurse training into higher education. In advocating that change, the RCN once led the world, but today many countries have overtaken us. In looking back at the obstacles which were put in the way of change—both within the nursing profession and by the government—we find that these obstacles are reduced or make the alternative options unworkable. The ability to spend more money meeting new needs by extending the old medical models of care is not an option. Diluting the standards of care is not an option. In short, carrying on as before is not an option. Nursing for all its shortcomings is now better placed to meet the new demands and more in tune with the philosophy of the women's and consumers' movements. There are international examples from which to draw and, more importantly, genuine political support from the public. I believe that the potential of nursing will have to be realised because it represents the last great untapped resource available to the politicians and the public to solve the dilemma of meeting new demands within cash limited NHS budgets. Nursing can meet and deal with the outside forces.

Nursing is one of the key functions in society with an essential social role and responsibility. Nurses and nursing, however, tend to be insular and narrow in their view of the world. I believe this is a serious weakness for nursing. It isolates us from the people we serve and contributes to our poor record of achieving political change for nursing. There are some steps which can be taken nationally, locally and personally which if they are taken by even a few will, I believe, build a body of wisdom and understanding of the outside forces working on nursing which is essential for future development.

Nationally

1. The reform of nursing education to broaden its content and move it into mainstream education.
2. Greater political participation by national nursing organisations in joint ventures with other health, consumer, voluntary, medical and political organisations.
3. Nursing in the health service should be sending managers into a wide variety of organisations to get insight into how they are run and the people they represent.

4. Nursing organisations should organise more conferences on social issues such as women, housing, poverty, old age and economic questions.
5. Publishers must realise that nursing has a perspective on social questions and provide more opportunities for nursing authors on social questions.
6. Through conferences and international travel we must tap more of the ideas and experiences from other nursing systems.

Locally

1. Hospital managements should establish annual rounds of lectures deliberately aimed at bringing speakers from outside medicine and nursing into the hospitals.
2. Nurse managers must develop their contacts with local consumer groups and women's groups, especially local councils and local political parties. It is not to be left to general managers, doctors or the public relations department.
3. Schools of nursing should encourage more lectures from outside and encourage debate between the different voluntary groups, councillors, etc. who have an interest in health services.
4. Local nursing organisations should make regular contact with voluntary organisations, health councils and local councils and political parties. They should encourage joint local work or events.

Personal

1. Participate in local politics and political parties.
2. Participate in nursing organisations.
3. Press managers for opportunities to examine wider issues in the hospitals.

References

Briggs, A. (1972) *Report of the Committee on Nursing*. London: HMSO.
Competitive Tendering Circular (1983) DHSS Circular HC(83)18. London: HMSO.

Department of Health and Social Security (1983) *NHS Management Inquiry Report* (Griffiths Report). London: HMSO.

Department of Health and Social Security (1984) HC(84)13. *Health Services Management Implementation in the NHS*. Management Inquiry Report. London: HMSO.

Green Paper on Primary Health Care (1986) *Primary Health Care: An Agenda for Discussion*. London: HMSO.

Judge Commission on Nursing Education (1985) *The Education of Nurses: a new dispensation*. London: RCN.

Platt, H. (1964) *Report of the Working Party on Reform on Nursing Education*. London: RCN.

Royal Commission on NHS (1979) London: HMSO.

Wood, R. (1947) *Report of the Working Party on Recruitment and Training*. London: Ministry of Health.

World Health Organisation (1978) *Declaration of Alma Ata*. Geneva: WHO.

CHAPTER 3

One profession

Those who regard nurses as a homogenous group, united by a universal philosophy of caring and a common body of knowledge, have been taken in by the stereotypes—and the optimism. Nursing's history is less that of a united profession pursuing common goals than of an assortment of different groups and specialist interests, each protective of their separate history and characteristics. This has given nursing a uniqueness and diversity, but it has also left nursing inherently weak as a profession, and lacking in stability in the political sphere. And, as I hope to show in this chapter, it has had a disastrous impact on nursing's ability to control its own destiny.

It is my hypothesis that the profession has only achieved minor progress when initiating changes: a new syllabus here, the establishment of a specialist type of nursing there. In contrast, the structure of the profession, and the role of the nurse as a health care professional, has almost all been determined with the help of external agencies, for example, the reports of Salmon (1966), Mayston (1969), Briggs (1972) and the 1979 Act. Clearly, there were also eminent nurses involved in effecting change, but it is difficult to refute the argument that nurses are the products of social policy and political forces rather than the initiators, as I have shown in the previous chapter.

Why is this? Is it because, as is commonly claimed, nurses are doers not thinkers, listeners not hearers, for is it possible to claim ignorance of the barrage of suggestions for change? Or are the reasons to be found in the structure of nursing, which hinders a constructively critical approach to change? Nursing has an apparent fear of the new and a reluctance to experiment and take risks, attitudes which become more and more fixed as frequent change is inflicted on nurses by external forces.

The reorganisations of 1974 and 1982 and, currently the implementation of general management (DHSS 1983) has imposed change on us, but has not fundamentally shifted attitudes. While we still await the full impact of this final imposition on the profession, it is already clear that its effect is far greater than nursing has ever imposed on itself. Some might argue that this is justifiable. Nursing should be the product of the society within which it is undertaken. Baly (1980) has argued this most cogently, and demonstrates quite clearly the formal relationship between nursing and society. This to some extent overlooks the nature of changes that have occurred within the profession. These are the changes about which society is not concerned.

To illustrate this, let us imagine the patient who arrives at the door of a health centre or hospital. As a general rule, that patient is not interested in the role descriptions of those working there, but is looking for a person he or she recognises as a nurse or doctor to deliver care. The patient is not concerned that the roles of health care professionals have, in some respects, changed out of all recognition over a period of 40 years. The expectation is that the most appropriate care will be delivered in the most skilled manner and by those best able to deliver it. We must admit, this expectation sometimes goes unfulfilled.

But from the profession's point of view, the range of nursing responses available to such a patient has increased enormously. For example, the immediate observations made on the patient in the late 1940s would have included temperature, pulse and respiration. The late 1950s saw the great debate about whether blood pressure should be taken by nurses. In the late 1960s, electrocardiographs were introduced into practice if the patient required them, and the late 1970s saw the debate about the nurse's role being expanded to include taking blood and giving intravenous medications.

Towards a Philosophy of Nursing

Bevis (1983) identified the principal problem the profession faces when determining a philosophy for caring, a philosophy which would be acceptable to all nursing branches. She suggests that four major philosophical systems have arisen from the historical setting of the profession.

The first she describes as asceticism. This dominated nursing beliefs and values for most of the nineteenth century and was typified by a great emphasis on the patient as a person whose spiritual salvation was more important than his or her earthly suffering. It emphasised self-denial and self-discipline for the nurse. Nursing came to have an air of vocation akin to religious life. In their day-to-day practice, nurses did not assert themselves. They were encouraged to devote themselves to their duties and to seek spiritual growth through hard work.

Romanticism supplanted this first philosophy from the end of the nineteenth century and became the dominant value system up to the Second World War. The emphasis was on emotions, the nature of experience and pursuit of the ideal. It encouraged loyalty to the doctor and idealised the schools of nursing. It produced in nurses a profound dependence on the doctor, and generated the idea of the nurse as a handmaid.

The reality orientation experienced by nurses with the onset of the Second World War caused a move to a value system based on pragmatism. This philosophy lays great emphasis on the practical use of objects—and even people—and the consequences of actions. Patients became known to the nurse by the type of condition they had and the bed space they occupied, rather than by their name and personality.

In the decade after the war, humanistic values began to be introduced into nursing, based principally on the work of Maslow and Abdellah. This caused nurses to be concerned about the whole person, especially in the context of the family and community from which they came, and increasingly the human being became central to nursing practice.

In the last ten years, a noticeable change of emphasis has occurred as existentialist principles have been grafted on to the basic humanism. Perhaps most problematical, has been the belief that the patient has freedom of choice. This means that they have the right to reject the advice and directions of health care professionals, no matter how good or necessary they are. The new emphasis is on caring, with the nurse first and foremost accountable to the patient.

It seems to me that the problem generated by these beliefs and value systems is that all four philosophies are currently present in nursing. I would suggest that their existence is the principal reason for the problem of achieving the underlying unity of purpose which is a prerequisite for effecting change within the nursing profession.

Nursing practice still relates closely to the medical model, but as nurses develop their own person-centred abilities and activities, so nursing may slowly distance itself from its medical linkage. The links with the medical model of care will remain strong, because many of the activities nurses undertake are, and will continue to be, directly prescribed by medical staff.

The important thing to note is that certain care areas are being perceived by all health care professionals as belonging uniquely to nursing. As this area expands, and the number of activities increase, so will the next great era of change be ushered in.

This leads me to consider unity. So far I have described barriers to change which are partly philosophical and partly structural. The concern now is for structured change, that will take the whole profession with it.

Divisions and Diversity

It was unthinkable that the 1979 legislation could not have referred to nurses, midwives and health visitors. But these and all other nursing specialisms are species of the same genus. They have a common set of characteristics that make them more like each other than like groups outside nursing.

This diversity, currently a weakness, could, if unified, be the profession's greatest strength. Of course, it is the RCN's belief that the profession will be stronger and serve society better if there is only one organisation for nurses called the RCN, but until then I suggest a change of approach, one that is typified by nurses looking for commonalities and responding to each other and groups outside the profession on that basis.

This could prove to be extremely significant. Not only would it move the emphasis from points of negative disagreement to areas of positive agreement, it would also help in the development of a creative and unified responsiveness to change. Most of us still have nightmares about how we almost lost the 1979 nursing legislation because of internal dissension (see Chapter 6). It sticks in my mind as a paradigm of what can happen when everyone is unified except our profession. Whatever the reason, it demonstrated how nurses seem to withdraw from taking major strides of professional development at the very moment when to continue would give them everything they had asked for.

To change, and to meet the challenge of change, the profession needs the most effective and efficient method of preparation. The proposals encompassed within Project 2000 (1986) and the RCN commission on education's report (1985), in particular, set their sights on tomorrow in order to keep in touch with today. It is no use waiting for the common danger which unites even the bitterest of enemies to initiate that change. The profession has already seen how it can be overtaken by events.

We tend to forget just how far Britain is the envy of many countries for its relatively united profession. This may sound far-fetched, but it is a point worth emphasising. In the USA for example, the profession has no one effective national body. The American Nurses Association has a membership smaller than the RCN and while its political work at federal level is outstanding, its power as a strong national force is dissipated by two factors. First, the emphasis in recent years has been on developing state associations with a large degree of autonomy and virtually optional involvement in the ANA. Second, the growth of specialist organisation in the USA has proceeded apace outside the ANA. Many nurses chose to use their spare professional and political energy within an association geared to meet their specialist clinical needs. This in many places has had the effect of rendering the ANA and even the State associations weaker and more divided than they should be.

This is a worldwide trend. Many national nursing organisations have failed to adapt their structure to accommodate this need for specific interest groups, and are now paying the price as the offspring grow up and are poised to push their parents out of the nest. The International Council of Nurses is very aware of this development at the international level, where strong specialist groups continue to be established outside the auspices of the ICN. The present membership pattern of one national nursing association for every country in ICN cannot easily facilitate any form of looser affiliation, and it is clear that this problem must be examined carefully. Work is in progress which may, perhaps, provide a model to help national nursing organisations with their own restructuring.

The RCN would never claim to have got it completely right, but its success in this difficult area has been at least partial. Various patterns of local and national membership structures have been tried over the years in an attempt to enhance the democratic base of the College and facilitate membership involvement. The Tavistock report (1973) created local centres, and associations and societies at national level. Most recently, Council has sought greater unity and strength locally by turning centres into branches. This is not merely a renaming process, but an attempt to bring the professional orientation of the College together with its trade union orientation. The two are not mutually exclusive (see Chapter 10) and the RCN Council believed it was time to create a structure which fostered this powerful combination. The advent of general management and the consequent changes in the pace of life in the health service precipitated these changes. It must be admitted, however, that not all members were enthusiastic about facing change in their own organisation when so much of their working lives were turned upside down and the old familiar patterns of nursing organisation were being broken up. The key appointment in this new local structure is the district convenor, a post now amalgamated with that of the branch secretary. It is both the symbolic embodiment of, and the practical solution to, this unification.

While the RCN is in one sense a collection of specialist clinical interests, it still reinforces its primary aim as a pressure group for and expert group on nursing generally. This may at times mean that separate specialist interests have to be put on one side in order to pull together an agreed policy. Without such a policy any talk of power becomes farcical, and outside agencies begin again to dictate nursing's agenda.

The College has by no means a monopoly of representation of specialist interests. Many groups such as the National Association of Theatre Nurses, and the Psychiatric Nurses Association, do well because they are single-interest and do not have to blend separate interests into a coherent whole. In addition, because they depend so much on the energies and efforts of volunteers, they sometimes command a high level of involvement and commitment, which in the College can get lost because of its size and complexity. Yet it is a pity that these organisations exist outside the College. However successful a single-interest group is within its own terms, it does not enhance professional power or credibility.

The government and health service managers love to play off

one group against another—that is the essence of politics. And nursing starts with a serious disadvantage by presenting such a chaotic face. The College's garden is far from rosy, but it is the best arena for nursing to sort out its internal dissensions before entering the negotiating chamber.

I make no apology for dwelling on this topic, because it is crucial to the political development of nursing. In the first volume of *Political Issues in Nursing* (1985) three of the six essays are concerned in different ways with nursing's warring factions. And just in case it is assumed that the unity arguments have been won, these chapters describe and explain the differences and divisions. But it is the historian's eye, rather than that of the politician looking at using power to achieve goals.

Power at Work

White's essay (1985), 'Political regulation in British nursing', is especially critical of the RCN's attempt to achieve consensus. Dividing the profession into the generalists, the specialists and the managers, White cannot apparently envisage strong, effective professional unity under the RCN's umbrella. She fears the continued hegemony of the generalists (because of the sheer number of 'ordinary' nurses) and the managers (because of their power) will cause nursing to 'squeeze out all professional minded nurses' or drive them to form splinter groups.

We have already seen how the RCN has largely managed to satisfy its specialists, the professionally oriented nurses, and to retain them within membership. Yet White maintains, quite inappropriately in the 1980s, that the College's power-base is its managers. Nothing could be further from the truth and it is simply no longer true that the minority voice has been suppressed in the interests of political impact. She concludes thus:

'All these political struggles were characterised by the desire of one group to achieve its goals against the wishes of another group. They demonstrate the conflict between the aspirations of professionally minded nurses and the needs of the matrons or nurse managers and the institutions to retain control and to endorse the common good by deskilling nursing and employing a generalist level of labour.'

I quote this in full because it is a harsh allegation, which I do not believe is justified. White uses three examples to support her arguments—district nurses, health visitors and the 1979 Act. It would have been convenient if events had turned out as she anticipated, but they have not. District nursing flourishes, re-inforced by a much improved training, achieved largely against the wishes of the managers and by an official re-emphasis on community health services. Similarly, health visitors within both the RCN and the Health Visitors' Association have retained, and indeed enhanced, their power in the NHS. And in retrospect the 1979 Act looks like a triumph for sectional interests rather than a victory for the nursing consensus. The ideal Act for the pro-fession would have given us a true *carte blanche* to reform nurse education. Instead, all three 'professions' were placed firmly in the title and district nurses, occupational health nurses and men-tal nurses all have a mention.

White's conclusion is that 'in a pluralist society the enforce-ment of a unitary policy, of consensus, inhibits change. A denial of conflicting values forces the smaller groups on to the periphery and, in extreme circumstances alienates them and their values'. I do not understand this conclusion. Every society, every institu-tion, every professional group can be described as pluralist—it is a meaningless word because it is so universal. Nursing history, right from the days of Florence Nightingale and Mrs Bedford Fenwick, has thrived on conflict. The pace of progress—at least that change in which the profession has controlled from within—has indeed been slow, but that can hardly be blamed on a 'denial of conflicting values'. On the contrary, I would argue that the profession has sometimes been over-zealous in heeding its specialist interests, perhaps because these have pushed their arguments harder and longer than the generalists.

A word about midwives. Recently midwifery has been very much more assertive in proclaiming its differences and seems set to separate itself from mainstream nursing. Within the Staff Side of the Negotiating Council, the Royal College of Midwives has become increasingly vehement in arguing that midwives should be rewarded more highly than nurses. And in its response to Project 2000, the RCM, while accepting much of the underlying philosophy, has rejected the very tactfully worded and tentative suggestion that midwifery training could be brought into line with the rest as a one-year course following the common foundation programme. This to me is a totally unrealistic and arrogant distinction which should be eradicated.

Moving On

What, then, is the way forward to achieve both unity and progress? First, it is important to shatter two myths which hinder progress. The first is that, in some sense, the profession is a caring and self-protective family. If one considers what happens when a specialist report is published or enquiry announced it can be seen that this is not true. Cast your minds back to the publication of the Jay report (1979). It was, and remains, the single greatest threat to the future of mental handicap nursing. It has generated the most divisive debates in that particular discipline of nursing. Some nurses argue for their own removal from this field of nursing while others feel ignored and neglected in large institutions under threat of closure.

Where is the support and reassurance from the rest of the profession proving that mental handicap nursing is part of the mainstream of nursing? Who are the nurses outside the discipline who have attempted to argue with those who wished to move that element of health care outside our profession? The sad truth of the matter is that most nurses have remained either ignorant of the development or apathetic to its implications.

Another example is the Cumberlege community nursing review (1986). It will demand great effort to make the whole profession realise that it is important for every one of us, and not just those involved in primary care. The danger is that because it is difficult to identify the threat, few will respond.

The second myth is that it is possible to effect a separation between primary and secondary care. For too long, discussions about nursing care have contrasted community with institutional care. To my mind this is a false division, both physically and politically.

The physical contrast between home and hospital is invalid because both are part of the same community. The only difference is that of location within the one community. The same types of health care professionals deliver the most appropriate care depending on their own training and preparation, irrespective of venue. The political distinction is invalid because the patient, as a member of society, has contributed to the cost of the health care he or she receives through national insurance and taxes. The patient relies upon health care professionals to determine the most appropriate medium for the delivery of that care. To the patient, it is one national health service, with one source of funding, but with multiple outlets.

I want to propose two possible ways forward. First, that we set about the task of clarifying our professional values and beliefs, and agree on a unified ideology. This is not a proposal which should be taken as encouragement to spend unnecessary time in philosophical star gazing. It is a suggestion that we seek to resolve the confusion we have seen in professional activities and strivings in recent years. The College has seen a massive increase in professional activity in all specialities. But this has been only the first stage in hammering out policy approaches and much remains to be done to achieve real improvements at patient level.

I want to see a co-ordination of professional activities which is of marked benefit both to individual nurses and to the profession at large, and therefore to the community we serve. This will require a programme of nationwide events to enable all nurses to participate. Part will be consciousness-raising, part education, and out of this will arise a unity induced by the effort of considering where, as a single profession, nursing should go.

Nurses have demonstrated in recent years, in many ways but notably through the RCN's representative body meeting, that instead of being the product of social policy, they wish to influence and even create that policy. We need to know therefore if the public views us as acting legitimately when we act in this matter, as we increasingly have done. The future direction of nursing must be one that is in harmony with the needs of society and with our professional aspirations. The choice is ours to make, and I believe that now is the time to make it.

I do not propose that we agree a unified ideology for its own sake, or to settle some academic argument, but because the view of society about health care is changing once again. For economic and social reasons, society is beginning to examine the way it provides health care, how much it can afford, and what role the professions should play. That timetable is much shorter than many seem to realise and unless we can enter the debate with the two essential ingredients I have described, then once again we risk having change imposed upon us.

Talk of 'unified ideology' and 'clarifying professional values' may seem to some to be pie-in-the-sky amid the hurly-burly of their everyday lives. Fine, you may be thinking, I believe in that, but what does it mean to me? I can see how the RCN in its grand Cavendish Square home can think such lofty thoughts but it's a long way from anything that will help me.

I sympathise with this. This chapter is based on a formal lecture I gave in 1985 and as such adheres to the conventions of such occasions. But I would like to add a note on something called rather pretentiously by our American colleagues 'networking'. This has a personal and professional as well as a political dimension but is worth mentioning at this point of the book because used properly it could help break down the barriers in nursing.

Nurses in Britain do tend to work in a compartmentalised way and are reluctant to find out about other parts of the profession or to seek the help or advice from others. Our American colleagues have no such qualms and whole books have been written on 'networking for nurses'.

I would like to make the following suggestions, principally in the interests of persuading nurses to share, support and find out about what is being done elsewhere. Reinventing the wheel is a common fault among nurses.

1. If you find yourself describing one particular specialty of nursing as 'not real nursing', think again. Nursing is what nurses do. Ring up a nurse in that specialty and find out more.
2. When did you last challenge your own prejudices and assumptions? We are all quick enough to challenge others, but a serious session of self-scrutiny can be most advantageous.
3. Next time you are planning a local event aimed at nurses in a particular specialty, pause to think whether bridges can be built and interests can be widened.
4. In social/professional situations, do you stick with your own or make a point of mixing? It's an effort but invariably worth it.
5. Hospitals are full of gossip, rumour and innuendo. Don't indulge in it. If you hear something on the grapevine that is directly relevant to your professional life, check it with a reliable source.

6. Remember how well doctors stick together in public—and mostly in private. There's more that unites nurses than divides them.

References

Baly, M. (1980) *Nursing and Social Change*. 2nd edition. London: Heinemann Medical.

Bevis, E. O. (1983) *Curriculum Building in Nursing—A Process*. 3rd edition. St Louis: C. V. Mosby.

Briggs, A. (1972) *Report of the Committee on Nursing*. London: HMSO.

Department of Health and Social Security (1969) *Report of the Working Party on Management Structure in the Local Authority Nursing Services*, Chairman: E. C. Mayston. London: HMSO.

Department of Health and Social Security (1979) *Report of the Committee of Enquiry into Mental Handicap Nursing* (Jay Report) London: HMSO.

Department of Health and Social Security (1984) *NHS Management Inquiry Report* (Griffiths Report). London: HMSO.

Judge Commission on Nursing Education (1985) *The Education of Nurses: a new dispensation*. London: Royal College of Nursing.

Ministry of Health, Scottish Home and Health Department (1966) *Report of the Committee on Senior Nursing Staff Structure*, Chairman: B Salmon. London: HMSO.

Neighbourhood Nursing: A focus for Care (Cumberlege Report) (1986) The Community Nursing Review. London: HMSO.

Nurses, Midwives and Health Visitors Act (1979) London: HMSO.

Tavistock Institute of Human Relations (1973) *An Exploratory Study of the RCN Membership Structure*. London: RCN.

United Kingdom Central Council for Nursing, Midwifery and Health Visitors. (1986) *Project 2000: A New Preparation for Practice*. London: UKCC.

White, R. (ed.) (1985) *Political Issues in Nursing: Past, Present and Future*, Vol 1. London: John Wiley & Sons.

Note: Parts of this chapter are based on the third Kathleen A. Raven lecture given by Trevor Clay in June 1985, entitled 'Unity for Change'. Extracts were published in the Autumn 1985 issue of *Lampada*.

CHAPTER 4

A question of conscience

Politicians of the Machiavellian school would wonder what a chapter on ethics is doing in a book about politics and power. 'Power gradually extirpates from the mind every human and gentle virtue', said Burke, so why allow conscience and fancy notions of moral behaviour to get in the way of the pursuit of power? Surely it is possible to separate the private and personal from the public and political, or at least to submerge individual values into the overall goal of the common good when nurses' political interests are at stake? Unfortunately it is not possible to make that kind of distinction. To pretend otherwise is a recipe for disaster on both fronts—the personal and the political. 'The personal *is* political' runs a favourite maxim of the women's movement.

Ironically, ethics and politics have tended to suffer the same fate among nurses. Both words seem to scare us. We have found it more comfortable to leave these areas to others or to compartmentalise them so that they are packaged into manageable chunks. Every nursing course and many conferences and study days have traditionally had a slot for ethical considerations, as if a lecture on the subject is enough to enable us to tick it off. Recently politics has gone the same way. The nursing cliche of the 1980s, 'nurses must become more political and develop political awareness', has ensured that every course and conference has a speaker on politics. And so we pretend that we are moving with the times and satisfying the demands of both ethics and politics in nursing practice. The reality is of course that this approach ensures that both are kept at arm's length, given a veneer of respectability and not allowed to permeate everyday life. They are not permitted to influence the way nurses behave or to help them towards coping with and dealing with their problems and dilemmas at work.

This is all the more disappointing when one considers how much ethical issues in health care are regarded as public property these days. Rarely a week goes by without television exploring ethical dilemmas in a medical context. When *This Week* asked the public, by means of an electronic voting mechanism, whether people who are HIV positive should be compelled to carry a card announcing the infection, the verdict was overwhelmingly in favour. Surrogacy, abortion and euthanasia are perennial favourites with the media and are subjected to regular scrutiny, not only in the Sunday religious and philosophical slots but in current affairs programmes too.

The theatre has also addressed fashionable health dilemmas, inviting audiences to explore their own beliefs and emotions. Who would have thought that a play about a bedridden, permanently handicapped young man (*Who's Life is it Anyway?*) would be a commercial success, but it was—on both sides of the Atlantic. *A Day in the Life of Joe Egg* by Joe Orton was an agonising play about a couple with a severely handicapped baby—now a classic. *The Normal Heart*, performed in a West End theatre, looked at the AIDS tragedy among the homosexual community. Never before has the public been so actively encouraged to participate in the debate on health dilemmas and problems.

The borderline between life and death can now be so indistinct. The press in 1986 seized upon the story about a young pregnant woman in Middlesbrough who suffered a brain haemorrhage and technically died. But her body was kept alive long enough for the baby to be delivered by caesarian and to stand a chance of surviving, premature though it was. The life support systems were then turned off and the deeply distressed and exhausted husband and father left to face the challenge of bringing up his baby daughter. The public, through this and other similar situations, often connected with organ donation, have a surprisingly full knowledge of the grey area between life and death, thanks to the attention it receives in the media.

But nursing ethics? Can there be such a thing? How is it different from medical ethics or indeed ethics generally? Many assume that because it is the doctors who decide when to turn off the ventilator, the lawyers who pronounce on issues such as surrogacy, the scientists who play around with *in vitro* fertilisation, and the managers and politicians who decide where limited health resources are put, then the nurses have no separate responsibilities.

And there is a supposedly sympathetic way of thinking that wants to keep nurses out of all this intellectual and moral agonising.

Castledine (1985) quotes the *Mail on Sunday*'s view of the nurses' role in a case of a severely brain-damaged baby: 'the nurses, decent caring people, devoted to the babies they look after in the ward, will not agree to what some believe is the kindest course—to remove the feeding tube. Who dares say they are wrong? Life is precious.'

So if the doctors are playing God, the nurses are the angels. They epitomise selfless devotion, caring and loving to the end and playing no part in any difficult decisions about life and death. Of course this is nonsense. These situations are difficult for everyone, but perhaps particularly so for nurses, who are the ones closest to the patient. The doctor comes and goes, the nurse is there round the clock. It is the nurse who gets to know the person, the personality inside a moribund body, even if brain-death has been certified and there are no apparent signs of life. Nursing ethics must relate, as Castledine concluded, to those situations and issues which specially, and sometimes uniquely, confront nurses. And this makes it a subject worthy of far greater attention than it has hitherto received.

I do not intend in this chapter to go over the familiar ground of health care ethics which are usually medical ethics—abortion, euthanasia, organ donation, surrogacy and so on. On these issues, there can be no special nursing view separate from the views that individual nurses might hold. In 1967 the Abortion Act, for example, gave nurses a conscience clause to enable them to opt out of participating in operations for the termination of pregnancy. This let nurses follow the dictates of their own consciences and might have been right at the time. But it also paved the way for discussion on other conscience clauses, for example, electro-convulsive therapy, and even AIDS, which begins to undermine the whole nursing ethic. There is no professional nursing view for or against abortion. The RCN, incidentally, nearly came a cropper in 1985 when it attempted to produce a consensus view from among its members on the Warnock Committee. It proved virtually impossible to put together contradictory comments from individuals into an overall corporate response. I hope the RCN will not fall into the same trap again.

I intend to look at areas that some would regard as far less exciting and glamorous, but which go right to the heart of the

ethical dilemmas nurses face—such as how to maintain the dignity of the patient, how not to show that you find a patient difficult, repulsive, ungrateful or stupid, when and how to blow the
whistle when patients are being treated in an unacceptable way,
whether it is ever permissible to disclose confidential information,
and so on. I have chosen these areas not only because these are
the day-to-day ethical dilemmas which nurses face, but also
because they have a political dimension. The political implications of ethical choices is a correlation which nurses must be
prepared to explore.

It is against this background that the RCN's Council decided in
1984 to set up a Committee on Ethics. Mary Armstrong (1984),
its chairman, described the kind of help the committee hoped to
be able to give: 'The conflict of loyalties faced by a nurse when
her medical colleagues, her employer or manager and the patient
seem to be simultaneously making conflicting demands on her;
the question of whether to tell when the safety of a patient seems
to require a breach of confidence or how to deal with a request to
be allowed to die from a patient.' Nurses, she added, need help in
thinking through their own personal prejudices.

The Committee, which has, not surprisingly, so far found it
hard to come up with the most effective way to provide this service for members, includes some quite outstanding outside members. Ian Kennedy, Professor of Medical Law and Ethics at King's
College London, was the author of a series of Reith lectures which
had a tremendous impact on the way the public view doctors and
medical power; and Julia Neuberger is a rabbi at the South
London Liberal Synagogue.

It is Julia Neuberger's articles on ethics and nursing which
have served best to put the Committee on the map. At the church
service which preceeded the 1986 RCN Congress in Blackpool,
Rabbi Neuberger spoke about how the Ethics Committee would
be producing guidelines suggesting options and drawing attention to dilemmas. 'In the last analysis however, the decision rests
with the individual nurse. *Lo tuchal ie hitalem*. You cannot hide
yourself or abrogate responsibility. The individual has to bear the
burden.' Her words show that she has grasped the essential
nature of *nursing* ethics more firmly than many nurses themselves. The full text is printed in *Lampada*, Summer 1986, and is
well worth reading for its clarity and perception.

If anyone had any doubts about the politics of ethics (rather than the ethics of politics—a very different matter), they should study the *Code of Professional Conduct* published by the United Kingdom Central Council for Nursing, Midwifery and Health Visiting (revised in 1984). This is presented very much as a living code, ready to be modified and added to as circumstances and opinions change. It has been distributed widely among nurses and discussed certainly among the more active sections of the profession. At the 1986 Labour Party Conference, Ann Keen, a delegate who was a nurse, waved it from the rostrum and declared that she intended to use it as a basis to report her nurse managers to the UKCC for negligence.

She could technically do this because the Code is quite specific in two particular areas. First, the nurse manager's professional accountability is defined as to 'have regard to the workload of and the pressures on professional colleagues and subordinates and take appropriate action if these are seen to be such as to constitute abuse of the individual practitioner and/or to jeopardise safe standards of practice' (Clause 11).

This marks an important turning point. Instead now of only clinical nurses being held to account for a misdemeanor, the manager who allowed an unsafe environment of care to continue and so contribute to the pressure on the nurse can be held responsible too. Second, the Code requires any nurse to draw attention to those places where safe standards of practice are endangered. Clause 10 states that accountability should have 'regard to the environment of care and its physical, psychological and social effects on patients/clients, and also to the adequacy of resources and make known to appropriate persons or authorities any circumstances which could place patients/clients in jeopardy or which militate against safe standards of practice.' The effect of these two clauses, therefore, is to place a professional and ethical responsibility on clinical nurses to report situations which are potentially dangerous; and as a corollory, to place the same kind of responsibility on the nurse manager, educator, or researcher to act if they are made aware of these dangerous situations.

The full implication of the Code in this respect has not yet been realised by the profession—perhaps even the UKCC is not yet ready to cope with the political implications of this document. For if ever there was a point where nursing ethics meets nursing politics it is here in Clauses 10 and 11. When in early 1986, during the RCN's Griffiths campaign, four proposed new NHS management arrangements were reported to the UKCC on the grounds that they would create an unsafe environment of care, the UKCC were clearly uncomfortable with this kind of 'political' activity. The RCN argued that the absence or dilution of nursing management skills in these structures would mean that patients could be put in jeopardy and clinical nurses would not have the professional accountability that was essential to safe practice. The let-out clause for the UKCC was evident very swiftly. As soon as some of the districts concerned knew they were in the political limelight, they put their house in order so that they could say with impunity that the RCN had simply got it wrong. Months later the UKCC replied to the College in terms so noncommittal as to underline its acute embarrassment over the whole episode. But for the College the success was twofold: the shock tactics in campaigning terms of naming names; and the metamorphosis of the Code as a political tool for nurses to use in a variety of situations.

Reg Pyne (1985) pointed the way to another use of the Code, more precisely to the statutory instrument which defines the respective responsibilities of registered and enrolled nurses. This is no ancient definition long hidden by the cobwebs of time, but on the contrary a newly drawn distinction which followed the 1979 Act. Pyne commented that so universally was the blind eye turned to this rule that it was clear the profession had quickly drifted into the 'institutionalisation of improper delegation'. He asked: 'Are there any hospitals left which only use enrolled nurses in the way in which that statutory rule intends? Are there any hospitals left in which the senior professional nurses do not use registered and enrolled nurses as interchangeable people when it pleases them?' These are rhetorical questions which are nothing short of dynamite. No-one yet has reported to the UKCC nurse managers who deploy enrolled nurses in roles beyond their competence, but it could be a useful weapon in the battle for educational reform which we chronicle in Chapter 6.

All these areas highlight the direct personal responsibility involved in these wider, more diffuse situations. Nursing has never known anything quite like this before. The fashion of the 1980s to talk about professional autonomy and personal accountability has taken a long time to move out from the learned papers and the conference rostrums into everyday life on the wards. Whatever we say about the personal stresses and strains on nurses—and they are considerable and largely incomprehensible to those who have not experienced them—we have not been good at apportioning blame, preferring to damn the system generally, rather than the decisions of individuals working to specific policies made by other individuals acting collectively.

Yet nurses are in the front line and no amount of buck-passing can absolve the individual from direct immediate, ethical involvement in many day-to-day events in health care. To reduce it to its basic—and nurses do not find it difficult to present these issues so dramatically—it comes down to two questions: who is to be allowed to live? And how is life to be lived and death to be experienced? The two are often agonisingly intertwined—the severely handicapped baby on the borders of life and death, the elderly person kept alive by a series of difficult and ultimately futile operations, or the decisions about organ transplantation.

Most people know broadly where they stand on these issues but the difficulties come as Chapman (1984) describes, when people do not obey their consciences or when one person's conscience dictates a different course from a colleague's. Ethical pronouncements, such as 'the intrinsic worth of man' and 'a moral basis for action' can only ever be generalised statements because there is not usually an absolute set of rules or a predetermined right course of action. So the pressure falls on the individual to distinguish what is in the realms of personal/professional morality and what can be attributed to the decisions of others. And the balance between these two is the decisive factor in answering the question, 'What can and should I do about it?' This is the point at which ethics meets politics.

Chapman concludes that the best guidelines for nurses are a belief (religious or otherwise) in the value of the person and 'a resolve to treat the individual as an end, never a means'. But in a concluding paragraph she says:

> 'the unsolved dilemma is when the choice has to be made between two equally compelling alternatives, kidney transplants or research into rheumatism, intensive care units or health education. Nurses may sit back and say that these are economic/political discussions and of no consequence to them. However, we are all responsible for the government we elect and hence, at one level, the choices they make.'

Can the health economists help us? An attempt has been made to provide a measure, but the facts and figures still do not entirely speak for themselves. The Centre for Health Economics at the University of York has explored the use of QUALYS (Gudex 1986) to put a figure on the extra life years and improved quality of life produced by a particular medical or health care intervention. Admittedly 'crude and experimental', the £ signs attached to various procedures have a peculiarly sobering effect. Maynard and Bosanquet (1986) explain that from, say a budget of £20,000 we can get one full quality of life year (QUALY) from dialysis compared to 26 QUALYs from hip replacement or nearly 120 from effective smoking advice by GPs. We may feel uncomfortable with this form of comparison, but when the inevitable cost consideration comes into society's decisions about how health resources are directed, then such a formula must be helpful.

To take the argument a little further, consider the conflict—which is bound to grow—between the demands of high-tech medicine and primary health care. Tempting though it might be to blame the medical profession solely for continuing to emphasise high-tech health care, I believe the situation is more complex. The public want a rapid, efficient health service, which generally means performing operations or prescribing the most effective drugs as soon as possible after the onset of an illness. If new drugs or, in Fleet Street terms, 'a medical miracle' is in the pipeline then the public want it, whatever the cost. Curbing these unfortunate demands is impossible and no table of relativities from the economists will pursuade them otherwise.

Here, indeed, does ethics meet politics. Dr Halfden Mahler, Director General of the World Health Organisation (quoted in Hall 1980) said:

'On one hand we have the persistence in terms of millions of people of such diseases as cholera and malaria, on the other, we have the gigantic modern machinery geared to the treatment of the whole range of diseases up to the point of obfuscating the distinction between life and death. In one sophisticated city more than 70 per cent of all so-called health expenditure is used on people who are going to die within the next 12 months. These examples reflect, in my opinion, an obsessional concern with marginal disease and tends to pervert the very concept of health.'

The Benthamite principle of the greatest happiness for the greatest number takes on a new dimension when applied to the division of health resources. But there is a massive public debate to be had before the argument in favour of primary health care can be won. How much ethical arguments are used and are effective amid the more traditional politico-medical conflicts about satisfying demand and pushing forward medicine's frontiers, remains to be seen.

The nursing role in this debate is obviously vital as it is at least as important an ethical issue as some of the more usual grandiose debates about abortion, euthanasia, clinical trials and so on. This is where, furthermore, nursing needs its managers and leaders, as far-sighted thinkers who can look beyond the immediate conflicts and pressures into a new system of health care, and begin to plot a course toward that new pattern.

One could say that ethics is about feeling comfortable with what is happening around you. How many nurses can say that? I want next to examine the nurse's personal and professional responsibility to speak out. Society generally does not much trust anyone who challenges the status quo, and nursing is exceptionally hostile to such people. In the deepest possible irony, nurses who kick up a fuss, lose their temper, or fight for patients' rights in an overt way, are often labelled deviant, stupid, politically extreme or—especially—unprofessional. Only nursing could find itself equating professionalism with acquiescence, subservience, silence and obedience. Members of other professions would take pride in a collective battle in which individual differences were subsumed into a common interest; or would respect an individualism which entailed the dogged pursuit of a point of principle. Nursing has seen very few crusaders and moral outrage is rarely permitted to rise to the surface. Fear of victimisation, of promotion prospects being jeopardised, of being labelled a troublemaker, all contribute to the wall of silence. We train nurses to accept discipline and to obey without question; we tend to undermine the natural self-assurance of young people and ultimately create a hierarchy in which no-one at any level feels easy about speaking out.

This reticence has proved a distinct political handicap. However interested politicians are in specific nursing and health-service problems, they can do little without evidence. The tendency to hide behind vague generalisations and incomprehensible 'nursespeak' can mean that politicians have little they can use.

We have found this time and again over such issues as the effect of financial cutbacks in the NHS, declining standards of care, and shortages of nurses.

Politicians and the press need hard facts and specific examples before they can highlight the issues and seek solutions. Even when it is in the patient's rather than the nurse's interest, nurses still have real difficulties in speaking out and naming names.

And all the signs are that in many places this is getting worse with the introduction of general management. Nursing's self-imposed wall of silence could perhaps be attributed to the desire to reinforce a favourable professional image, to keep the service running smoothly, or to avoid frightening patients or potential patients. But a wall of silence built by others is a different matter—and is certainly perceived as a dangerous development by those nurses who experience it.

Some local RCN members who attended a fringe meeting organised by the College at the Conservative Party conference in 1986, for example, said that they were concerned about what might happen if their general manager found out they were there. This, of course, is all the more ironic because it was not some dubious left-wing group, but the Tory Party itself. A unit general manager in Birmingham wrote to the editor of *Nursing Times* asking that only articles endorsed by the district general manager or a unit general manager should be published. This would apply to all articles describing service development and would ensure that the health authority's views are 'accurately reflected'. The picture throughout the country, therefore, is one of growing censorship in the NHS as part of the government's campaign to portray the service in a more positive and electorally appealing way. Nurses will find an increasing difficulty in reconciling certain ethical dilemmas with continued job security. Ethics meets politics.

In this environment, how can the nurse act as the patient's advocate? Some would say that this has never been more than pie in the sky. Brown (1986), for example, argued recently in *Nursing Times* that advocacy is a totally unrealistic notion in the nurse/patient relationship and even if it were not, it would not in any case be a desirable responsibility. Yet whether or not it is labelled as advocacy, nurses who have spoken out in the interests of a particular patient or group of patients have seen it as a natural extension of their nursing role. Their motivation was personal, not political—although it was often misunderstood and the cause of enormous personal and professional damage.

Jim Smith, when district nursing officer for Brent in North London, put on the record his 'ethical tightrope' when faced with implementing financial cutbacks. He asked:

> 'Just what does a nurse manager do as a responsible member of society, a committed nurse, and a member of the major professional organisation representing nursing in the UK? As a citizen with a social conscience and an active member of the RCN, I have made a number of statements to the press, to television and to radio. As a DNO I have given advice on the implications of government policies. This is my responsibility and my right.'

The result was that his regional nursing officer suggested he was upsetting the DHSS and should, in the interests of his career, be more careful. Needless to say, Mr Smith did not change his tune and continued to speak out according to his conscience. He refused to accept the view that the personal and the managerial could be separated: 'For me the person and the manager are the same rational human being.'

Jim Smith displayed a rare courage. Even though theoretically it should be easier for an experienced, well known and highly respected manager to blow the whistle, speaking out at this level can bring its own dangers. For one thing, it is unusual. Nurse managers, even before the changed climate of general management came about, did not have a good reputation for speaking out publicly on these or other matters. The reason was quite simply that involvement—however slight—with a mental hospital scandal, a well publicised inquiry, or even a difficult managerial situation could blight a manager for years. I could name several talented nurse managers who became so blighted and whose careers subsequently failed to thrive through no fault of their own.

How much more courageous therefore must be the whistle-blowers further down the line. Still by far the best work on the subject is Virginia Beardshaw's *Conscientious Objectors at Work* (1981) which looked specifically at the difficulties and dangers faced by nurses who complain about patient abuse in mental hospitals. She studied the whistle-blowers at a number of the notorious hospitals which have been the subject of inquiries; and described the harassment, victimisation and ridicule that often followed. But as well as supporting those who speak out, she has sympathy for those who are forced to remain silent.

'Nurses have good reasons for keeping quiet about abuse in mental hospitals: silence is a normal, human response to intimidation and fear. Their silence is enforced by vested interests within the hospital organisation—interests which have something to hide or which prefer not to face embarrassing, painful and difficult truths,' she wrote. She went on: 'This enforced silence involves a denial of basic human rights. Through it, patients suffer within a "caring" environment. Through it caring nurses are deprived of free speech and are effectively prevented from following their profession's basic tenets.'

She ends on a constructive note, arguing that since our institutions will continue to be filled with increasing numbers of elderly and dependent people it becomes imperative to create a climate where free speech can flourish. She urges:

- Greater acceptance of the notion of nurse advocacy.
- Guidance by management and health authority members for staff.
- Improved handling of complaints.
- Better understanding by trade unions of staff who complain.

The book undoubtedly caused a stir when it was published, but it didn't change the world. Skilfully, it had a message for everyone involved in the Kafkaesque world of the large mental hospitals—the staff, managers, health authority members and the unions. Everyone nodded sagely and thought either: 'There but for the grace of God go I', or 'It couldn't happen here!'

In the mid-1980s, the problem is changing. As the vast Victorian institutions are gradually closed down and many of their residents moved into community care, the environment of care is changing and bringing with it different kinds of pressures. Providing a more normal lifestyle in a homelike setting is a laudable aim but often the staff are not qualified nurses and therefore not professionally accountable, and so the smaller-scale provision can bring new forms of abuse. The relationship between carer and cared for can become more claustrophobic so that malpractice is less easily detected. Financial exploitation is a real risk and the residents can find themselves with a less interesting and stimulating style of life than in hospital. This is not, of course, an argument against care in the community, but rather a warning that the exploitation of and cruelty to patients in long-stay institutions is not automatically abolished when the hospitals themselves are bulldozed.

Virginia Beardshaw did not change the world, but her work was important. Four years on, the National Association of Health Authorities in England and Wales published *Protecting Patients* (1985) which contained guidelines about how to complain. How far this booklet has been disseminated and has reached those who have real need of it is impossible to tell. But Reg Pyne, Director for Professional Conduct at the UKCC, writing in the RCN's student magazine *Tradimus* (1986) said it was often still the students who were at the front line in these situations.

Students are particularly vulnerable. Their fresh approach, keen eye and frequent moves around the wards mean that they witness the kind of behaviour that others may no longer notice. Yet their lowly position in the nursing team makes them reluctant to complain lest they are accused of being pushy troublemakers and end up with a poor report from the ward sister or charge nurse; or worse, discontinuation of training. The whistle-blowers in the mental hospitals have often been students—for example, Ken Callanan at Brookwood Hospital. It would be gratifying to say that we have moved into a more enlightened era where students' comments and observations are listened to and acted upon. But this is not so. NAHA's guidelines, the UKCC's Code of Professional Conduct, the strengthened arm of the Health Advisory Service and the health ombudsman are all now contributing to a more open environment in the health service, but the whistle-blower is still a deviant who is usually treated abominably.

The mental hospital situation has been well documented and always attracts a great deal of publicity once the whistle has been blown. Less sensational are some of the areas of nursing ethics which are a more recent preoccupation. For example the debates about confidentiality of records, which during the passing of the Data Protection Act (1984) extended well beyond the computer and into the all kinds of information about patients and who does what with it. As Keighley (1984) pointed out, since doctors now spend less and less time with patients, the nurse's role in using information about patients becomes all the more crucial. 'While a doctor may decide on occasions what information should be released when—it is the exception rather than the rule. In this field the nurse has moved to centre stage.'

This has tremendous implications for nurses faced with difficult decisions about how much a patient should be told about their diagnosis and prognosis. The nurse's professional judgement and conscience may dictate one course when the doctor has decided on another. The wishes of the patient and his or her relatives have also to be taken into account, often building into a tangled web of half-truths, hints, misunderstanding and guilt as nurse, doctor, patient and relative weave their intricate patterns.

Nor does it stop at the bedside. In health care, there is no such thing as totally confidential information, and it could well fall to the nurse to decide whether certain circumstances might require disclosure of information given in confidence. This is not so far-fetched, since it might encompass a situation where there is legal action or crime, or an investigation into a complaint, or ethically approved research, a risk to public health or national security. Again, in these areas ethics meets politics.

Nursing does not, therefore, have a good record on facilitating discussion of ethical issues. The one-off lecture, the compartmentalisation and the intellectualising of ethics in nursing has served to deprive many nurses of the chance to explore and argue through many of the agonisingly difficult situations they encounter in their work.

Inhibitions about opening up on these issues and uncertainty about how to translate these beliefs and feelings into political action has created a dual frustration which, if allowed to take hold, serves to increase levels of stress and feelings of depression.

But these common complaints voiced by nurses could so easily be removed by creating a more sympathetic environment where nurses felt their ethical views, personal feelings and professional aspirations could be aired without the threat of victimisation, ridicule or misunderstanding.

Checklist for Whistleblowers

(Compiled by D. Biklen and M. Baker.)

1. Identify your issues carefully. Prioritise them.
2. Document the problem thoroughly. Double-check your information. Gather statistics, memoranda or other data to

support your position. Make sure you are right. When considering the problem and its solutions, ask yourself who is creating the problem? Is this person or group vulnerable? What is his/her 'Achilles' heel'?

3. Report the problem to your immediate supervisor.

4. Re-contact the supervisor if there is not action. Keep a record of this.

5. If there is no action or only token action taken, consider the implications of whistleblowing in this situation.

6. Identify who will suffer if the problem goes unchanged. How much suffering will occur? Be able to speak knowledgeably about the costs of inaction. Who benefits from continuation of the problem? Is someone's prestige or economic welfare being fed by the continuation of the problem?

7. Know and be able to refer to the ethical standards of your professional association.

8. Identify the laws and regulations which relate to the problem at hand. Identify organisational mandates, official policies, statements of mission and philosophy which support correcting the problem.

9. Identify an internal sounding board, a counsellor with whom you can share your concerns, and from whom you can receive good advice. Be sure to select a person you can trust.

10. Identify informants within the hierarchy of the organisation who can keep you informed of what is happening in the chief administrative offices, and in other key locations of the organisation.

11. Develop private and public support, allies (eg lawyers, professional experts, associations, consumers, citizens). School yourself on advocacy agencies and consumer groups in your community. Find out which groups have a reputation for sustained action.

12. Show the right decorum. You will certainly offend others by the substance of your complaints. Therefore, one should not offend by style (swearing, wearing bizarre clothes, attitudes of arrogance, etc.).

13. Warn your family and closest friends that you may become the object of slander (rumours may start about your religious or political beliefs, about your sex life, about your mental health, your professional competence, etc.).

14. Examine your needs. Ask yourself if you are willing to go through perhaps a good deal of suffering because your cause is right and just. Understand that you may not win. Anticipate your own suffering. Project yourself into the future. What will you do when you are rejected? Will you need personal and other forms of support? How and where will you get the needed support? Also understand that some change occurring as a result of the efforts of a whistleblower is never associated with the person who originally blew the whistle. Someone else who took little or no risk may get the credit when you took all the risk. Ask yourself whether you have the stamina for blowing the whistle. Do you have the energy to see the effort to completion?

15. Develop an action plan.

16. Optional: alert the organisation that you are going public. Allow enough time for the organisation to remedy the situation before making your move.

17. Blow the whistle. Go public. Focus on the issues and not on the personalities involved. Keep the issues limited in number. Do not go public on more than one issue when the issues are not mutually supportive of one another. Select issues which are compatible with contemporary cultural norms. In other words, do not select issues for whistleblowing that society at large has not yet accepted as valuable.

18. Go public as a group if possible. Have a plan to keep the issue alive in the eyes of the public. Often, a single news conference will not generate sufficient momentum to keep the issue alive in the community.

19. Be prepared to propose an answer to the problem you have exposed.

20. Know how much you are willing to compromise.

21. Be a hard worker: keep evidence of your own competence. Do your job thoroughly. Make sure you cannot be criticised for being incompetent in your job. This point is critically important and a prerequisite to any whistleblowing if you are to have credibility.

22. Whenever possible, strive to win. Whenever possible, choose winnable issues.

23. Keep a record of your whistleblowing activities. Learn from your own experiences. Share your experiences. Have access to a competent attorney in the community who will offer

you advice about protecting your legal rights as an employee.

24. Enlist others to whistleblowing. Establish dialogue and on-going communication with others who have the moral conviction essential to whistleblowing. Establish ongoing relationships with people who blow the whistle responsibly, consistent with the points outlined in this checklist. Teach effective whistleblowing strategies to others.

(The Development Disabilities Rights Center, through which this checklist was developed, is a programme of the Mental Health Law Project and the Center on Human Policy, Syracuse University, 216 Ostrom Avenue, Syracuse, New York 13210, USA. The checklist is reproduced with the kind permission of the University.)

References

Armstrong, M. (1984) Everyday Ethics. *Lampada*, Autumn 1984. RCN.

Beardshaw, V. (1981) *Conscientious Objectors at Work—Mental Hospital Nurses: A case study*. London: Social Audit.

Brown, P. (1986) Who needs an advocate? *Nursing Times*, August 6.

Castledine, G. (1985) Who's playing God? *Nursing Times*, June 12.

Chapman, C. (1984) What is good? A basis for action. *Journal of Advanced Nursing* 9:315–18.

Data Protection Act (1984) London: HMSO.

Hall, D. (1980) The nature of nursing and the education of the nurse. *Journal of Advanced Nursing* 5:149–59.

Gudex, C. (1986) *QUALYS and their Use in the Health Service*. University of York, Centre for Health Economics.

Keighley, T. (1984) The right to know. *Nursing Standard*, Sept. 6. RCN.

Maynard, A. and Bosanquet, N. (1986) *Public Expenditure on the NHS—Recent Trends and Future Problems*. London: Insitute of Health Services Management.

Neuberger, J. (1986) What is Nursing Ethics? *Lampada*, Summer 1986. RCN.

Protecting patients: Guidelines for handling staff complaints about patient care (1985) Birmingham: National Association of Health Authorities in England and Wales.

Pyne, R. (1985) Trends in accountability. *Senior Nurse* 2 (2), January 16.

United Kingdom Central Council for Nursing, Midwifery and Health Visiting (1984) *Code of Professional Conduct*, 2nd edition. London: UKCC.

CHAPTER 5

Hierarchy and hands on

It does not take much political acumen to fix upon one particular area where politics and nursing will meet head on in the next few years: standards of care. The nursing profession has taken on the government of the day on several occasions to allege that standards of care were declining and the NHS was in a state of crisis. We were listened to politely and maybe ultimately we contributed to increased resources for the NHS—but I am not sure we really ever got the message across in anything but a transitory way.

I can attribute this to three main problems. First, however meticulous the research and careful the presentation, there is always in political terms the impression of 'those nurses at it again'. In the final year of the Labour government the College compiled *An Assessment of the State of Nursing* (RCN 1978) and then early in the life of the second Tory government came *Nurse Alert* (RCN 1984). In between these formal presentations, nurses kept up a steady barrage about low morale, shortages of staff, declining standards of care. If the NHS was in crisis, then it was clearly in the politicians' eyes a dynamic kind of crisis because services continued, people remained grateful for the work of the NHS, and staff apparently still wanted to contribute to it. The crisis argument did not work. And why not? Principally because nurses are copers; they do not often complain: they get on with the job.

Second was the problem of evidence. Doctors from time to time resort to shroud waving to get their message across. This, combined with skilful use of statistics, such as 'a waiting list of 2,000 people', '20 operations cancelled this week through shortage of staff' created an impression of sound dossiers of evidence. Against this, the nursing crisis seemed vague, unquantified and therefore intangible in political terms.

Third, and by far the most serious problem, was the reluctance of nurses to stand up and be counted. It could be that eventually the UKCC *Code of Professional Conduct* (see Chapter 4) will change this and give nurses the official backing to speak out directly and specifically about unacceptably low standards of care in their working environment. But it is hard to admit defeat in this way and most nurses would rather soldier on, complaining behind the scenes, rather than tackle the central issue of inadequate resources and back-up.

To begin to be more effective in this area nurses must be able to quantify the problem and, equally, be able to explain why it matters. Facts do not always speak for themselves and to explain the significance of doing something—or not doing it—does not always come easily to nurses who are probably used to a different way of working. Consultants in the high-tech areas of health care do not seem to find it hard to go public when their work is threatened, even if their justification is shaky and their facts thin.

I will in this chapter try to show how facts can be collected and used to good effect, and how the standards of care issue is beginning to take off in a way unheard of in previous years. But one central and fundamental change must take place: the ability and the motivation to communicate effectively. This means not only presenting arguments in a way that the rest of the world understands, but presenting the whole issue of standards of care in a way which interests and involves the entire nursing profession, not just those at the academic or managerial top. Gobbledegook reigns supreme in the standards of care lobby. Now every professional is entitled to a modicum of gobbledegook, but he or she must be able to distinguish between legitimate professional shorthand and incomprehensible, pretentious nonsense.

Here is an example of our problem: 'This study was founded on the premise that a lack of content validation in the initial design stages of quality assessment research was sufficient to have led to the non-significant correlations between structure, process and outcome variables reported in the literature.' I will not quote the source; suffice it to say that this is from the abstract of a paper dealing with promoting a concern for standards of care among nurses. Surely we must do better, for our own sakes let alone anyone else's.

The Changing Scene

So far in this book, I have set the scene in a general sense. Now I want to be specific about how the pace is changing and why we cannot procrastinate any longer about this key issue. The College has for years rather proudly cited its work on standards of care (RCN 1980, 1981) and the clinical career structure (RCN 1981, 1983), as valuable contributions to the ongoing debate. But it is now clear that good and sensible documents are not enough: setting standards of care remains as elusive as ever, and the clinical career structure a mere chimera. The debate may be ongoing but it must take heed of the changed NHS environment and the new political pressures—and speed up its activities.

General management is a symptom rather than a cause of this changed environment, but it is undoubtedly its most obvious manifestation. The Griffiths Inquiry (1984) signalled the demise of professional power in the NHS. The doctors were deemed important only in so far as they could be nudged into managerial positions and thereby be best placed to control expenditure by other doctors. It was a clever political move, not intended to curb clinical freedom directly, but to circumscribe it as much as possible. The nurses were deemed monumentally unimportant—barely mentioned in the report itself except for a whimsical reference to Florence Nightingale—and only briefly mentioned in the associated notes.

The profession was in fact given the assurance, enshrined in these notes, that 'nurses would still lead nursing'. At best on that fateful day in October 1983 it was an ambiguous message given the undoubted primacy of the new general managers; at worst it was a shrewd attempt to lull nurses into a false sense of security. Two or three years later it is clear that the attempt to separate professional leadership from the managerial is workable—just—on paper but totally impracticable in real life.

I raise the Griffiths situation for two reasons. First because it has undoubtedly wrecked the plans the profession had for changing its leadership profile. The RCN documents *A Structure for Nursing* (1981) and *Towards a New Professional Structure for Nursing* (1983), pulled together with such enormous care and attention to detail, have now a rather dated quality. Not only do they inevitably envisage a situation where nursing has a guaranteed place in the management team, but they also imply that nursing has control of its own destiny. The former is now certainly not the case, the second has always been doubtful. Now nursing has to take what it can get in a managerial sense—an appalling situation, but one which would have been much worse had the College not pulled out all the stops in a major campaign in 1986 to spell out why, for the sake of the patients, nursing's power and influence needs to be retained in the NHS. Our victory was partial, but the battle was well worth fighting.

The theme of our campaign was standards of care and the way in which an effective nursing voice in NHS management and health policy making must be sustained in the interests of good patient care. This was a difficult correlation to make because the public hardly knew that nurse managers existed, let alone understood why nurses could be helped to give better care by the right nurse managers. Our advertising agency did us proud in drawing these parallels in a way that was dramatically impressive for the public. Six months later the public still remembered the advertisements about general management we ran in January and February 1986. In a nutshell, therefore, nursing has lost its guaranteed power bases in management and plans for a clinical career structure, let alone an ideal managerial structure, are back on the drawing board. When a substantial number of hospitals have no nurse manager above ward sister/charge nurse level, it becomes painfully easy to be wise after the event and to wish that nursing had pushed through what it knew was right while it still held the reins.

The whole first point is about the impact of general management on nursing structures. The second point concerns the philosophy which came with, and now permeates, much of the public sector. The light of the new managerialism shines through Griffiths, rooting out waste and inefficiency, cutting through bureaucracy and humbug, speeding up decision making, curbing the power and influence of the professionals, projecting a positive image of the NHS, and so on.

The health service's new breed of general managers has a list of five items in the Filofax. First there is Value for Money (already abbreviated to VFM). This may sound like an innocuous blend of Samuel Smiles and Mrs Beeton, but it has already, through such devices as the Rayner Scrutinies, permitted general managers to go where others feared to tread, for example selling off 'surplus'

NHS staff accommodation, cutting back on recruitment advertising and making changes to nurses' shift patterns. The service is reeling from some of these measures. The continued pressure from the NHS Management Board for general managers to make more and more efficiency savings has meant the quality of care argument has become very difficult to put forward.

Second on the list is the associated device of performance indicators, a new management tool to help determine whether various services are being delivered as cost-effectively as possible. It includes comparisons between the relative costs in different health authorities, to give high-cost districts some hints about how far they should reduce their costs. The implications of this for quality of care are again very serious.

Third comes competitive tendering of ancillary services, notably laundry, cleaning and catering (DHSS HC(38)18). This is a policy which at first sight was difficult to contest and most nurses approached it with more or less neutral feelings. But this changed in many places when the results were seen in terms of unfair treatment of ancillary staff, uncertain savings and a marked deterioration in the standards of service provided. The RCN's advice pack for members (RCN 1985) contained a form for reporting inadequacies in the provision of support services. I do not believe most nurses have an ideological stance on this issue; they were simply goaded into action by what they saw around them.

Fourth comes quality assurance, the general manager's counterbalance to the relentless quest for efficiency savings. This term, borrowed from industry, has become the usual riposte to accusations of declining standards and levels of service. Many nurse managers have taken on quality assurance responsibilities across the whole service and are beginning to take up these reins. Standards of nursing care must clearly be a part of this, though under the quality assurance/general management banner it is doubtful it will be quite the same study as it was when it was wholly in nursing hands. I will return to this later.

The list concludes with performance-related pay. The NHS Management Board places great store by this as a means of encouraging general managers to achieve their goals in the allotted timetable. The enormous flaws in this were described by Winkler (1986) but it is clearly here to stay for general managers and perhaps eventually for other NHS employees. If it ever reaches nurses then tension between quality and quantity could reach snapping point.

These five elements go to create the new management milieu and it is against this background that nursing must revamp its work both on the clinical career structure and on raising standards of care. Equally important, the close interrelationship between the two must be recognised and reinforced.

The Story So Far

'How good is your nursing?' asked the then RCN President, Sheila Quinn, in the launch issue of *Lampada* (1984). Summarising the work so far, Dr Quinn reminded us that the starting point for the College's initiative on standards was requests from members via the stewards for measures or indicators to show when the quality of care was unacceptable. *Towards Standards*, published and well promoted in 1981, did not provide this but it did hint at a fundamental dichotomy between the existing nursing hierarchies on one hand, and the notion of individualised patient care given by nurses accountable for their actions on the other. On one hand, for example, we label the ward sister/charge nurses as the key to setting standards, and on the other we ascribe to all qualified nurses new individual responsibilities. The project may have started out with the idea that a series of measures could be relatively easily produced, but certainly before long, nursing's raw nerve was touched. We are still waiting for the indicators and measures (although some nurses are already using existing methods with satisfactory results), and I suspect that the hierarchy problem will have to be resolved before new initiatives on standards can be successfully made.

The College's standards of care group had opted for a conceptual framework already adopted by the Manitoba Association of Registered Nurses in their famous standards of care work (1981). This uses the criteria of structure, process and outcome (Donabedian 1966), emphasising the whole environment in which nursing care takes place and the responsibilities of managers, educators and researchers, not simply the clinicians. The problem is primarily one of language: however many down-to-earth examples are produced, those particular words do not inspire nurses who are looking for practical help within a readily comprehensible framework. I suspect 'structure, process and outcome' may have to be shelved and more penetrable guidelines produced, if standards of care work is to inspire the majority of nurses.

How far have we progressed towards a clinical career structure? As we show in the next chapter, nurse education has been a series of action replays over the past 50 years. So it is with the clinical career structure—a succession of high-level recommendations for a new structure that would better reward financially and professionally nurses who stay in clinical nursing have come to nothing. The Committee on Nursing first proposed a two-tier nursing sister grade in 1972, a proposal reinforced two years later in more specific recommendations from Lord Halsbury. But this has rarely been used imaginatively to reward clinical specialism. When Clegg (1979) recommended over-the-odds increases to ward sisters he thought he was doing largely what the profession wanted him to do. But he did not bargain for the wrath of the nurse managers who resented the erosion of pay differentials and were suspicious of even this modest attempt to start a clinical career structure. This phenomenon has cropped up time and time again to prevent change—rarely in an overt way, since arguments are usually found to oppose the changes without resorting to naked self interest. It is the syndrome which runs, 'of course they should earn more, but not more than me'.

Nurse managers had, until the Griffiths Inquiry, done exceptionally well in reinforcing their positions as leaders in health care. Salmon (1966) and Mayston (1969) gave nurses their management career ladder which made their incorporation into management teams after the 1974 reorganisation a natural progression. A career structure for clinical nurses would help tremendously in stemming the excessive wastage rate of qualified nurses from the NHS. Very few places have made creative use of the interface between the ward sister and nursing officer grades—an opportunity which was handed to the profession on a plate. The terrible irony is that now the old hierarchies have been broken down by the arrival of general management we may stand a better chance of getting that elusive career structure.

New Objectives

I want next to explain the basis of my cautious optimism. First, the troubled history of the nursing process has left us with, in most places, a system of individualised patient care which is used with varying degrees of conviction and effectiveness. The traumas of the late 1970s and early 1980s are over and the basic idea of nursing care being assessed, planned, given and evaluated according to an individual's needs is now established even if the phrase 'the nursing process' is thoroughly discredited.

Combine this with a much wider acceptance of professional accountability, reinforced by the UKCC's Code of Professional Conduct, and we have fertile ground for new initiatives on standards and career structures. Pearson's work in Burford and Oxford based on his book *The Clinical Nursing Unit* (1983) will, I believe, assume increasing importance over the next few years as the profession grapples with these difficult issues. Among the many challenging ideas that Pearson discusses is how to make primary nursing a workable reality in this country.

Primary nursing—in a modified form if necessary—is, I believe, the key to the achievement of a qualified nursing workforce (see Chapter 8). It knocks the old hierarchical system and the old thinking on standards for six. Not to be confused with primary care nursing, it means that the primary nurse holds round-the-clock responsibility for planning and organising the care of a group of patients. She can only provide actual care when on duty, so at other times it is provided by an associate nurse. She would also be qualified and may also be the primary nurse for other patients. Various modifications of the system are possible, indeed necessary in order best to meet the requirements of the health care system and of the particular ward or unit (Manthey 1973). This is indeed ripe territory for the 'yes, buts' and the 'what ifs' of this world, but whatever the final details, the principles of primary nursing must be worth seriously considering in the fight for higher standards and a more rewarding pattern of working for nurses. Very tentatively, *A Structure for Nursing* in 1981 mentioned 'the primary nurse' but this radical idea was never developed further.

Also drawn from Pearson is some sound work on standards of care, which, while academic, is also acceptable to clinical nurses. Because all this work on clinical development has had to be evaluated as it progressed, Pearson used an existing scale, Qualpacs (Wandelt and Ager 1974), which makes use of direct observation of patient care. This is obviously not a tool to be used every day, but as a means of comparing standards before and after certain changes took place it is excellent. Pearson has built this kind of evaluation into all his work, surely a unique achievement.

What else gives me grounds for hope? Project 2000 in its overall philosophy aims to improve standards of care by training and educating more effective nurses. More specifically, the proposals open the way to the beginnings of a clinical career structure, with the new idea of a registered nurse practitioner as the main caregiver and the specialist practitioner having taken further courses in hospital or community. The idea of a more flexible upper clinical grade is most appealing and the Project 2000 proposals should be slotted into the other discussions which are in progress.

Furthermore, the work of the Staff Side of the Nursing and Midwifery Staffs Negotiating Committee, of which the RCN is a part, is beginning to bear fruit. I think at one time, the Review Body itself was—off the record—impatient with the Staff Side and the Management Side for not moving ahead on the clinical grading review. But work did get seriously under way during 1986 and 1987, and proposals were drawn up which are intended to form part of the Staff Side's evidence to the Review Body in November 1987. These twin initiatives, one rooted in professional and educational concerns, the other in gradings and remunerations, show how the two sides of professional trade unionism came together and moved forward on both fronts.

Two problems loom. One is that while the arrival of general management has opened up new opportunities for rethinking the relationship between clinical nursing and management and for creating a more satisfactory structure, it is by no means guaranteed to win the hearts and minds of the nurse managers still in conventional posts. Their insecurity following such massive changes in their work responsibilities could well mean that they are reluctant to facilitate change. The assumption that nurses in management and education are superior to those in clinical posts still pervades the profession and if it is not blotted out, it will again prevent these vital reforms from going through.

The second problem concerns the government. Clearly, the work on the clinical grading review is being watched very carefully. The Minister for Health, Tony Newton, is on the record (1986) as saying that the profession might not get everything it wants: 'I would ask you not to build your hopes of achieving everything you want too high for I think both sides may need to compromise on some points dear to their hearts.' Politics is, of course, all about compromise, but it did seem a little premature to urge us to trim our sails even before the ship has left harbour. There will undoubtedly be cost implications in the short term, but if a more satisfactory way is devised to hold people in clinical nursing—both financially and in terms of job satisfaction—then the long-term benefits and savings will be enormous. Nursing has had so much change imposed on it from the outside, let us not lose this vital development from within.

Finally, my grounds for optimism are built on real confidence that the standards of care bandwagon throughout the country is beginning to roll again. One major stimulus, as I have mentioned, is the new emphasis within the NHS on quality assurance and the appointment of nurses into many of the new quality assurance posts. Another is the continuing concern among clinical nurses about declining standards and a poorer level of service as patient throughput is increased. The circumstances may have changed, but the dissatisfaction among nurses is the same: they feel they cannot give the quality of care that patients need.

The College's work on standards culminated in 1983 with a publication on standards-setting which was used internally to stimulate further discussion among specialist groups. None of this, it must be admitted, has penetrated very far into the profession, so it remains an enormous challenge to the RCN's Alison Kitson to get this new phase of the work out of the committee rooms and into the wards.

Dr Kitson was appointed in 1985 to head up the RCN's Standard's of Care project, following her outstanding work at the University of Ulster, where her doctorate looked at the therapeutic role of nurses caring for hospitalised elderly patients. She has already shown that she can combine the academic and practical in a way that is nothing short of charismatic—and her use of language when speaking to nursing audiences promises well for the long struggle to communicate these ideas.

Speaking at a conference in Hartlepool in 1986 she made tactful mention of the uphill task:

'Nurses are still relatively unaffected by any of the discussions that took place. Our newspapers and professional journals continue to uncover poor practice, our own profession is straining under the increasing pressure of cutbacks and increased patient throughput, and while we are still anxious and concerned about standards we do not seem to be able to find what we are all searching for.'

She and her project team, backed enthusiastically by the College Council, have recognised the urgency not just to complete the academic work, but to spread the word with practical help and guidelines 'to grip the hearts and minds of every nurse in the country'. A generous donation from the Royal National Pension Fund for Nurses has given the project a flying start and I am sure that some important and valuable publications will come out of it.

The Standards of Care work is essential both for the development of the art and science of nursing and in nursing's political sphere. In the second half of the decade, we will not be able to get away with a report such as *Nurse Alert*, sound, well argued and compelling, but fundamentally anecdotal. The experiences of nurses will always count for something in this kind of campaign, but in the era of general management we must meet facts with facts. We have to do our homework, to be able to compare actual practice with good practice, to use figures to reinforce the argument, to show that nursing has worked out for itself what is acceptable and what is not. The political dimension of quality of care will become more and more crucial as the financial pressures on the NHS grow, as they undoubtedly will under any government. Let us ensure that the ammunition is ready by the time battle commences.

Plan of Action

Sadly for nursing, the central concerns outlined in this chapter—providing an incentive to stay in clinical work and finding ways to improve the quality of care nurses are able to give—have become cliches about which many are now cynical. Work in both spheres is now under way with an energy and widespread commitment and involvement the like of which we have never seen before. How can we ensure that this time round it works and our goals are achieved? In the political domain, here are a few essential steps on the road to change:

• To devise a framework for quality which is universal in its applications, flexible in its approach and comprehensible to busy nurses who do not have time to digest piles of research.

- To devise a strategy for action to explain the framework, encompassing the whole profession and using all kinds of devices to invite participation.

- To get nursing research working for us at last; to get it off the library shelves and into wards, clinics, health centres, offices; to turn it into wallcharts, checklists (yes, checklists), strip cartoons and so on. Perhaps the greatest piece of nursing research ever is Doreen Norton's Pressure Sore Calculator.

- To look at how general managers do things and get on their wavelength to influence their thinking.

- To learn the techniques of quality assurance and find out what nursing can learn from this wider sphere.

- Never to forget that we are no longer an enclosed profession, but one which is working in the floodlight of public and political scrutiny.

References

Donabedian, A. (1966) Evaluation, the quality of medical care. *Milbank Memorial Fund Quarterly* 44 (Part 2, July): 166–206.

Department of Health and Social Security (1983) *Competitive Tendering in the Provision of Domestic, Catering and Laundry Services.* HC(83)18. London: HMSO.

Kitson, A. (1986) Standards of Nursing Care. 5th Ruth Langton Memorial Lecture, Hartlepool. Unpublished.

Manthey, M. (1973) Primary Nursing is alive and well in the hospital. *American Journal of Nursing* 727(1):83.

Pearson, A. (1983) *Clinical Nursing Unit.* London: William Heinemann.

Quinn, S. (1984) How good is your nursing? *Lampada,* Autumn 1984. London: RCN.

Royal College of Nursing (1985) *Contracting out of Services from the NHS: Advice to members.* London: RCN.

Royal College of Nursing (1984) *Nurse Alert.* London: RCN.

Royal College of Nursing (1978) *An Assessment of the State of Nursing.* London: RCN.

Royal College of Nursing (1980) *Standards of Nursing Care.* London: RCN.

Royal College of Nursing (1981) *Towards Standards.* London: RCN.

Royal College of Nursing (1981) *A Structure for Nursing* (1981). London: RCN.

Royal College of Nursing (1983) *Towards a New Professional Structure for Nursing.* London: RCN.

Standards of Nursing Care (2nd edition: 1981), Manitoba Association of Registered Nurses, Canada.

Standing Commission on Pay Comparability (1979) *Report No. 3, Nurses and Midwives* (*Clegg Report*). London: HMSO.

Wandelt, M. and Ager, J. (1974) *Quality Patient Care Scale.* New York: Appleton-Century-Crofts.

Winkler, J. T. (1986) NHS spur for the spurious. *The Times*, October 14.

CHAPTER 6

Education

The single most important issue facing nurses in the 1980s is the political battle to achieve the reform of nursing education. At its May 1986 meeting the RCN's Council put this at the top of the agenda, as its highest priority for the decade. This is an unprecedented decision, representing as it does unanimity among an elected cross-section of the profession.

The political battles are of two sorts. First is the internal struggle to weld the profession together. Each of the specialist groups such as paediatric or occupational health nurses must be convinced that their distinctive needs are being met. Each of the broad areas of nursing must be sufficiently convinced of its value to them—the clinicians, the educators and the managers. Then the major branches of the profession (which breaks up when it suits them into three separate professions), nursing, midwifery and health visiting, must be convinced that their uniqueness would be recognised and minority groups protected. Finally, to use a broad categorisation, the 'trade unionists' and the 'professionals' in nursing must be somehow reconciled in a belief that both nurses and patients will be served equally well by the changes. This does not only apply to the divide between the health trade unions (COHSE, NUPE and so on) and the professional organisations, but also to the divide within the College itself, the generalists and the specialists as White (1985) has described them.

The second political battle is the external one, not on this occasion to achieve a major legislative change, but to persuade the government that the extra financial cost and the inevitable manpower disruption of reforming nurse education will—in political terms—be worth it. This is not a battle that will be fought solely on the plains of Whitehall. On the contrary it has all the elements of a full-scale theatre of war encompassing many separate socio-political groups because there is widespread consumer interest in nursing and health care issues generally; trade union interest in keeping nursing's doors open as wide as possible to workers of varying educational achievement; and the higher and further education lobby's interest in increasing its stake in nursing and health-related subjects.

The bottom line is, of course, to persuade the Treasury to allocate additional resources to nurse education, but in pursuit of that end many separate and apparently disparate arguments will have to be won. Celia Davies, Project Officer for the UKCC's Project 2000, wrote in *Rewriting Nursing History* (1980):

> 'Education requires resources. Sufficiently powerful people must believe sufficiently in the worth of allocating resources to education if anything is to change. It is not just a matter of a budget to pay teachers, it is a matter also of providing equipment and facilities, of releasing learners for the classroom, of teaching potential teachers to teach and, if the learning is of a vocational sort, of interrupting the daily practice of the skill in order to provide opportunity for learners to learn.'

This was written long before Project 2000 was conceived, but I am sure those words rang in Ms Davies's head as the work of persuading people of the value of change proceeded month after month. Davies's comparative study of nurse education in the UK and the USA reveals very different patterns of development, but a common trend of perennial shortage of resources and the intervention of economic and political interests to the disadvantage of nurses.

I do not intend in this chapter to spend much time on arguing why educational reform is now urgent and vital. The evidence for this is well covered elsewhere in the book. The main thrust here is to discuss the political issues involved in these changes and to plot a political course for the next few years, as Project 2000's fate unfurls.

Learning from the Past

Hegel's wise words about history are totally apt for nursing education: 'What experience and history teach is this—that people and governments never have learnt anything from history or acted from principles deduced from it.' A succession of reports over the past 50 years have either been misunderstood, ignored, or only partially implemented. Crystal clear, far-sighted recommendations such as those in the Wood Report (1947) were watered down, not primarily by the government but by the profession itself—or sections of it—anxious to preserve the system, nervous of radical change and determined to move only as far as they were pushed. This phenomenon, worthy of further examination, shows how internal politics are at least as significant as the external. Having completed his work as chairman of the RCN's Commission on Nursing Education, Dr Harry Judge said in a *Lampada* interview (1985): 'I do believe that when nurses say what they want in terms of the education they require they will get it, and until they do, they won't.' Behind this polite expression of exasperation, Dr Judge is hinting that achieving professional unanimity is a higher mountain to climb than that of political agreement on a broader sphere.

The fate of the Wood report, set up by the Ministry of Health to review the position of the nursing profession in the light of two previous inquiries, Athlone (1938) and Horder (1943), is well charted by Able-Smith (1960). The report proposed that schools of nursing should be separated from the hospitals and put under powerful regional training boards. The training period would be shortened to two years, but in this time students would be educationally oriented, with an 18-month course with a common core, followed by six months specialty training.

Like Judge, 40 years on, Wood argued that this separation of education and service would reduce wastage by a third or a quarter. It was calculated that the 20,000 extra staff needed to replace student labour would be found from reduced wastage, the shorter training, greater use of married staff, part-timers, male nurses and nursing orderlies, but not of enrolled nurses.

The government gave very serious consideration to these plans to separate education and service, and in 1949 the Nurses Act set out to change the character of the General Nursing Council by weakening the power of the matrons. It also empowered the Minister to set up standing Nursing Training Committees, though with less power than Wood had envisaged. The Act gave nurse training its own funds and attempted to loosen up the system to allow the General Nursing Council to facilitate Wood-type experiments in the move towards reforming nurse education.

Needless to say, without the profession's whole hearted support proposals were so diluted and the manpower crisis so pressing in the 1950s that the central core of Wood was lost and the unhappy compromise of training and service continued.

It was not lost because the government opposed it, but because the profession's power bases—the RCN and the GNC's—rejected the key proposals. White (1980) shows how the RCN's response to Wood, drafted by a sub-committee, was substantially amended by Council so that it rejected the Wood notion of student status. It also rejected the idea of shorter, but more focused training and insisted that the matron should remain firmly in charge of nurse training.

Matrons, especially those from the teaching hospitals, dominated not only the RCN Council at this time, but also the General Nursing Council, which disapproved of much of the Wood Report. It rejected the shortened training but thought that students could be supernumerary for a short period. Like the RCN, the GNC wanted the matron to remain in charge of the school of nursing. As White comments: 'There is an inescapable feeling of disapproval emanating from this memorandum, a primness and a preference for the maintenance of the status quo.'

White's important analysis of nursing politics in this period concludes that only the Horder Report has real relevance for today. She regards Athlone and Wood as 'recipes for their own day'. I disagree—and so clearly does the Project 2000 team. Horder envisaged a hierarchical clinical team with the enrolled nurse as the main grade and the SRN as the 'officer'. The SRN elite with their educationally oriented course would be the profession's leaders; the enrolled nurses, the workers. White sees this concept of the team as relevant today with the use of the nursing process, the registered nurse doing the planning and the paperwork and the enrolled nurse carrying out the plan. In the six years since White wrote it, much has happened and, as we show in Chapter 8, the highly pressurised wards and community services do not now lend themselves to this kind of demarcation. The future—in terms of efficiency, quality of care and the nurses' own job satisfaction—lies in primary nursing. And for this the vision of Wood, although not now with the shortened training, is far more applicable than Horder.

In the history of missed opportunities, surely the fate of the Wood report deserves a chapter of its own. A more courageous handling of its proposals might have given a very different nursing profession in the 1980s.

And then came Platt (RCN 1964), set up in 1961 by the RCN to consider the whole field of nurse education. It reported three years later, proposing an apprentice system for pupil nurses, but full student status for students. It echoed Wood in proposing a two-year course of theory and controlled clinical experience. The third year would be spent working, but closely supervised. A few experimental schemes were set up under the wing of the GNC, but generally Platt fell flat without even stirring as much political interest as Wood.

So who killed Platt? The report included a scheme for putting its proposals into action, being mindful of the financial implications. Less sensibly it also made mention of the fact that the function of the GNCs would have to change if this new style of training were implemented. Davis (1978) shows how Platt was published in the same year as another College report, *Administering the Hospital Nursing Service—A Review*. The overall intention was for the two reports to be taken together as a plan for developing nursing. But the government chose to run with the managerial reforms and the profession realised that changes on both fronts simultaneously would not be possible. Hence, in 1966, came the Salmon Report and education had to wait until Briggs in 1972. 'To channel energies into administration rather than educational reform was maintaining the status quo', argued Davies. But the report's death knell was well and truly sounded on the evening of its publication, when a well known matron appeared on television to say that student status wouldn't work. So an RCN report was effectively killed by the nurse managers who were concerned above all else about staffing the wards.

Once more, radical educational change was avoided and the profession found stopgap solutions to ease its problems. Training for example, became more 'educational' with the introduction of a new syllabus for general nursing in 1969, the implementation of which preoccupied the nurse education world for some years. When in 1970 the first part-time course for mature students was introduced, it was regarded as another innovative way of slaying the manpower monster.

This 'triumph' of gradualism in nurse training has been described by Davies as 'a series of small concessions slowly gained but no real challenge ... to the basis of nurse education'. The

NHS inherited the legacy of the 1930s and earlier, when the 'initial compromise' in nurse training ensured a low cost, virtually invisible system. I agree with Davies's surmise that throughout this period the student labour system was unchallenged and 'the history of the NHS in respect of providing facilities and staff for nurse education continued to be dogged by that compromise without ever addressing it directly'.

So the 'heroes' of nurse education were not enlightened men like Sir Robert Wood and Sir Harry Platt, but those who tinkered successfully with the system to shore it up a little longer. And the villains of the piece, those who ensured that real educational change in nursing that would give both student and patient the kind of deal to which they are entitled, are kept firmly behind the scenes. And then there was Briggs (the Committee on Nursing 1972). The irony was that it should have been necessary for the Secretary of State for Social Services to invite Professor Asa Briggs to review the role of the nurse and midwife and their educational needs. Professor Briggs started work just six years after Platt reported and came up with a set of proposals which, while structurally more radical than his predecessors', were considerably more conservative educationally. One might therefore have expected them to be adopted rapidly, but 15 years on we are still waiting for educational reform.

From Briggs came, in 1979, in an eleventh hour dash before Parliament was prorogued, the Nurses, Midwives and Health Visitors Act. This created the UK-wide statutory body which Briggs recommended and opened the door to educational reform. For, unlike its statutory predecessors, the UKCC was given the responsibility 'to establish and improve standards of training and professional conduct for nurses, midwives and health visitors.' The fruit of this is Project 2000.

Before gradualism is again allowed to triumph, let us remember the profession's public disarray during the passage of the 'Briggs' Bill, as it was consistently, though inaccurately, called. Roland Moyle, Minister for Health, and chairman of the ironically titled Briggs Co-ordinating Committee, was the epitome of patience and compromise as he watched—clearly with a growing sense of amazement—nursing's leaders display their political ineptness.

Nursing Times (1979) marked this period of nursing's history with a series entitled, 'Tales of Mystery and Imagination', which set out to record for posterity the splits and rivalries played out during those few months. So engrossed was the profession in tearing itself apart that it failed to notice that parliamentary time was running out.

Sheila Jack, who was one of the champions of the health visitors' cause at this time, commented: 'It was a great pity we couldn't sort ourselves out before it reached parliament. But then on the other hand, knowing all our entrenched attitudes, it possibly had to go to parliament so the whole thing could be thrashed out in the open and debated by people who aren't nurses.' The profession survived that catharsis—just. But I don't think we can in future afford to put our professional destiny quite so naively in the hands of the politicians.

The need for unity within the profession I have covered elsewhere. Here I will simply reiterate that if that kind of warfare can break out in public, in parliament over a statutory framework which should simply have been seen as a broadbrush enabling piece of legislation, then what hope is there for achieving unity for the next great hurdle—educational change?

A New Dispensation

What happened between 1979 and 1986 when Project 2000 (UKCC 1986) was published? The RCN Council, reflecting its members' impatience with the pace of gradualism, and at a request from me, set up in December 1983 its own Commission on Nursing Education (1985), chaired by Dr Harry Judge, Director of the Department of Educational Studies at the University of Oxford. The College's Council, its predecessors not noted for their enthusiasm for radicalism, was hoping perhaps for another dose of gradualism more in the tradition of Briggs than of Wood. After all, things were, in the Whig sense, getting better. Nurse training was becoming ever more educational, experimentation in styles of training was in progress, entrants were more highly qualified than ever before and teachers were seeking degrees and growing in self-confidence.

But Dr Judge dealt a body blow to gradualism when he argued vigorously and uncompromisingly for the wholesale move of nurse education into higher education with, of course, the associated prerequisites of supernumerary status, a broader-based common core curriculum, and a simpler pattern of qualifications. He wrote: 'Palliatives have been proposed, but the underlying conviction of this report is that nothing less than fundamental reform can now be effective. The changes which are proposed will appear to many as dangerous and threatening, but should not (for that reason alone) be rejected. Failure to undertake radical changes will, in any case, be even more dangerous.' Council received the report with unanimous enthusiasm and adopted it as RCN policy.

Many nurses do not see themselves as having any relationship to higher education. It appears distant, alien, elitist and irrelevant. It means academic dedication and brains. It means 'A' levels. It means universities and degrees. Apart from the minority who actively choose a school of nursing rather than a university course, most recruits turn to nursing because at school they have been labelled nice, full of common sense and hard-working. Nursing and higher education form an alarming, slightly comical juxtaposition which takes a bit of getting used to.

I had my first taste of higher education when in 1976 I was seconded to do a masters in social administration at Brunel University. I underwent a tremendous metamorphosis. Interestingly, the students tended to be differentiated more by life and work experiences than into those who had degrees and those who did not.

But the higher education which Judge envisaged is altogether more hospitable. Let me shatter a few myths. First, wholesale transfer to higher education and supernumerary status does not mean the removal of student nurses from the wards. Clinical experience will still play a major part in the course, but instead of its being dictated by service needs, it will be educationally controlled. Second, it does not mean the nursing will become an all graduate profession. The suggested qualification is a diploma of nursing studies which, validated by the Council for National Academic Awards, will mean something academically (unlike the RGN and other qualifications at the moment) and enable nurses to build more easily on their basic qualification throughout their career.

Third, it does not mean that only the universities can help. Higher education's web now stretches much wider to encompass the polytechnics and colleges of higher education together with the central institutions in Scotland. While universities have done badly in financial terms, the other parts of higher education, being more vocationally and scientifically oriented, have moved to centre stage. The government's Green Paper on Higher Education (1985) certainly emphasises this direction as the way a Conservative government will move in future.

Fourth, it does not create a new elite—and to reject higher education for these reasons is fundamentally to misunderstand these proposals. It would simply be giving to those same kind of young people who opt for nursing at the moment a better chance to learn the skills of their chosen profession, a less stressful environment and a more useful qualification at the end of it. It would be the same people, except that we would want to train fewer of them because the drop-out rate would have declined.

Would higher education want us? Nursing's intrinsic inferiority complex will always pop up and ensure that nurses are kept isolated and away from the mainstream of anything. If nursing went into higher education, it would overnight change the face of polytechnics and colleges. For one thing it would double the number of women in most of these institutions, and for another, nursing would form the largest study group. So rather then being concerned about what the higher education milieu will do for nursing, it is more relevant to ask what the nursing milieu will do to higher education.

Yet it remains to many a frightening solution to nursing's manpower and educational problems. So a new form of gradualism has arrived in the form of the ENB's proposals (1985) and, of course, Project 2000. The UKCC's analysis of the problems of nurse education and its proposed solutions are almost the same—in essence—as the RCN's. But instead of opting for the logical conclusion of higher education, Project 2000 refuses to be specific, and ultimately—after setting out its own criteria—leaves it to the National Boards. Project 2000's Chapter 7 is uncharacteristically imprecise, recommending new links with educational colleagues outside nursing through 're-establishments, partnerships and the formation of education consortia'.

Within its enthusiastic response (RCN 1986) to Project 2000, one of the RCN's few major criticisms was about this reluctance to seek wholeheartedly a future in higher education. The College argues that the main planks in the UKCC's policy—supernumerary status, separation of service and education, a common foundation programme—will be harder to achieve within the present system than they would be within higher education.

The RCN said:

'The UKCC's view of developing partnerships with colleges of higher and further education and a variety of provision based on existing schools of nursing would ultimately prove to be the harder option as a hotch-potch of local arrangements would develop without central intiatives and agreements. This would be disadvantageous to the student and the health service alike since it would be impossible to secure a mutually beneficial, nationally agreed transfer of resources and responsibilities. It would mean that the education to which student nurses are surely entitled may elude them once more and nurse education would remain its backwater.'

It believes it would be disastrous for nursing and the health service if schools of nursing were encouraged to build local educational relationships without central agreements as to the status of the student, the cost of the courses, the accountability of the tutors and so on. The better educational deal we are seeking for young people who choose nursing would not be served by this kind of loose alliance. The danger would be of creating a second-rate day release course where on Tuesdays and Thursdays nurses became students and spend the day at the local polytechnic. This will not fool young people who want to gain a useful and worthwhile qualification like nursing, but in a genuine educational setting. Likewise I would not want to see nursing's precious educational budget plundered by greedy college principals seeing the local school of nursing as easy game. The world of higher education finance is a monumentally complex one in which individual schools of nursing, eager for increased contact with mainstream education, could be taken for a ride.

When Lord Horder during the war said: 'Given a liberal outlook and a careful, planned curriculum, the training of nurses in this country could be developed into one of the great national education movements for women,' he was speaking at a time when girls' education was ill-developed and short on science and mathematics. But 45 years later we are still looking for that great movement, especially in terms of higher and further education which is still woefully short of women. We should not lose yet another opportunity to create this better educational deal.

The education of nurses is of broad social concern. Nursing in the UK takes the single largest group of qualified young women who leave our schools. The exclusion of nursing from higher education in this country is the main reason for the participation by 18 year olds and the female participation rate in higher education being among the lowest in the industrialised world. It is time that educational reformers and women's rights campaigners woke up to this major issue. Its neglect lies at the very heart of Britain's apparently poor educational statistics.

Nor should it be underestimated how much more attractive to men the profession could become if its recruits are properly educated. A college-based course alongside others in the natural and social sciences could make nursing far more approachable for young men who would not otherwise have thought about it as a career. And as the manpower crisis bites, it will become vital to recruit more men into the profession.

There is, after all, nothing remarkable in educating nurses within higher education. Most other English speaking countries in the developed world do it—and a few in the developing world too. An over-emphasis on college-based education in the USA is to be avoided since American traditions of both higher education and health provision are so very different from our own. But a number of countries have made the switch more recently and, candid about their problems and their mistakes, they do not regret it. Israel, Australia, New Zealand, Canada and Norway are newcomers to higher education who are facing the inevitable short-term problem of staffing the wards. Turkey, Kenya and Nigeria are already well on the road to a higher education course for their nurses.

The self-confidence of the Australian nurses in fighting politically for this change is impressive. Bottorff and d'Cruz (1984) show how nurses in Australia have been seeking the public's acceptance of their move into higher education. Rather than tell the public that nurses have decided this is their goal and that it will ultimately be good for society, a dialogue has been opened to share the problems and work in a participatory way towards a solution. They argue that nurses are 'accountable to the community to keep pace with changing health needs' and their case must be argued through with the community. 'The aim is not to sell, win or bludgeon a community into accepting a principle or change', but to achieve a negotiated, common-based decision.

Radical Solutions

In Britain, as we have often said, our problem is less about winning the public's support than about achieving agreement within the profession about the way forward. The disagreement between the RCN and the UKCC about where nurse education should be based is mere sophistry when compared with the clash between the UKCC (and the RCN) and the unions over the very basis of Project 2000. The National Union of Public Employees, for example, cannot accept the shift of emphasis that Project 2000 entails and sees the proposed introduction of the 'aide', replacing the 'nursing auxiliary', as a 'deskilling of basic nursing' which 'pulls up the ladder' and drops the auxiliary off the bottom.

The union raises the spectre of the government using the Youth Training Scheme to fill the wards with young people undergoing so-called training. 'The prospect of highly qualified nurses spending their time chasing 18/19 year olds around wards to try and get them to empty bed pans must be one that even the Project Group would baulk at', says NUPE.

The union also wants the retention of the enrolled nurse, but with the present misuse and abuse of this grade removed. And the Confederation of Health Service Employees (COHSE) similarly rejects the 'aide' grade and wants a new second-level nurse intro-duced, much along the lines of the Briggs proposals for an intial 18-month training leading to a certificate of practice. NUPE, while welcoming some parts of the report such as supernumerary status, rejects many of the central proposals as 'narrow and elitist'. COHSE describes it having 'a pronounced bias to convert-ing nursing into a primarily white, middle-class profession'. Needless to say, the unions firmly reject the College's policy of a wholesale move to higher education and are at pains to empha-sise that not only should close links with the service be main-tained, but nurse training should also remain firmly rooted in the NHS and students should remain salaried employees.

I challenge these views—a prime example of how so-called radicalism is really ill-disguised conservatism, criticising the status quo and yet arguing for its retention. The present system of training and education, and the division of the nursing workload exploits every member of the nursing team, including the staff nurse. Salvage (1985) chronicled this most effectively in *The*

Politics of Nursing, but was in the end not so strong on plans for reform and realistic solutions.

It can only be the rigid application of political ideologies which leads to the view that Project 2000 is elitist and racist compared to the present system. I believe the existing pattern of nurse training and the hierarchies of nursing are riddled with social and educational injustice and are themselves racist. The largest number of people from ethnic minority groups are to be found in the auxiliary and enrolled nurse grades, and are subject, as we have seen, to quite unacceptable abuse and misuse. Many enrolled nurses began their pupil nurse training not because they were incapable of the educational attainment needed for student entry, but because they were not made aware of the advantages in career terms of the three-year training. Only when their two-year training was well under way did they realise that their qualification led nowhere. How can any trade union support this sytem?

A single point of entry to the profession must surely be the most just way of restructuring nursing. If one accepts that there can be no logical way of dividing up nursing into 'simple' and 'technical' tasks then the need for a single grade of practitioner becomes imperative. But rather than seeing this as creating an elite—an officer grade as Horder described it—it is working towards a fairer, more egalitarian system. It may certainly mean that the registered nurse has to step down from her pedestal a little: she will no longer have several layers beneath her—she will be it. 'And who will do the work?', ask the radicals. The qualified nurse will do the work and—if other reforms ever see the light of day—she will also have a revolutionised way of staying in clinical nursing and of progressing in salary terms, as we show in Chapter 5.

As essential corollary of this is the need to find ways to give young people who are educationally disadvantaged the opportunity to enter nursing. While I understand why 5 'O' levels is used as a minimum standard entry, it should not be seen as a monument to professional elitism. A reasonable standard of literacy and numeracy is essential in nursing today with the growing importance of record-keeping, the increasingly complex drug dosages and the need to keep up to date with research and new thinking. By lowering entry standards we do no service to anyone: the patient could be endangered and the nurse could well find herself unable to cope with some of the responsibilities which are vital to good nursing care.

Sitting examinations for the sake of it can appear a waste of time to many young people. But, if they are sufficiently motivated by the desire to go into nursing, the 5 'O' levels becomes a means to an end. As a slogan I once saw in the United States put it: 'For the job you want, get the education you need.' Of course, it is not solely a question of motivation; much more needs to be done to provide the key 15–18 age group with more opportunities to collect those necessary 'O' levels. Perhaps the further education sector might like to revamp the old-style pre-nursing courses to fill this particular gap.

Finally then, let me chart the path to educational reform:

- Continue the battle to ensure that nursing is portrayed accurately to the public, so that there is better understanding of why nurses need to be well educated.

- Resist the temptation to be panicked by the government or health authorities about shortages of staff. Reducing entry standards or further diluting the qualified workforce are short-sighted solutions which are doomed to failure.

- Open the dialogue with higher education about means and ends.

- Correlate the health problems of the 1980s with the need for a widening and deepening of the nursing role—and for nurses who can work flexibly and intelligently.

- Reach out to the politicians' own agenda—a better health service, an improved deal for women, a more respectable and useful higher education sector.

- Remind people that vets are trained in higher education!

References

Able-Smith, B. (1960) *A History of the Nursing Profession.* London: Heinemann Educational Books.

Bottorff, J. L. and d'Cruz, J. V. (1984) Getting the public involved in tertiary change. *The Australian Nurses' Journal.* 13(11):47–9.

Davies, C. (1978) Four events in nursing history: a new look. *Nursing Times* occasional paper 74, no. 18.

Davies, C. (ed.) (1980) A constant casualty: In *Rewriting Nursing History, Nurse Education in Britain and the USA to 1939* pp. 102–122. London: Croom Helm.

The Development of Higher Education into the 1990s (1985) Department of Education and Science. London: HMSO.

Dunn, A. (1979) Tales of Mystery and Imagination. *Nursing Times*, May 31.

English National Board for Nursing, Midwifery and Health Visiting (1985) *Professional Education/Training Courses: Consultation Paper.* London: ENB.

Interim Report of the Inter-departmental Committee on Nursing Services (Athlone Report) (1938) London: Ministry of Health.

Judge Commission on Nursing Education (1985) *The Education of Nurses: A New Dispensation.* London: RCN.

Lampada (1985) Interview with Harry Judge, Spring.

Nurses, Midwives and Health Visitors Act (1979) London: HMSO.

Reports of Nursing Reconstruction Committee (Horder Reports) (1942, 1943, 1949) London: RCN.

Report of the Working Party on the Recruitment and Training (Wood Report) (1947) London: Ministry of Health.

Report of the Working Party on the Reform of Nursing Education (Platt Report) (1964) London: RCN.

Report of the Committee on Nursing (Briggs Report) (1972) London: HMSO.

Royal College of Nursing (1986) *Comments on Project 2000.* London: RCN.

Salvage, J. (1985) *The Politics of Nursing.* London: Heinemann.

United Kingdom Central Council for Nursing, Midwifery and Health Visitors (1986) *Project 2000: A New Preparation for Practice.* London: UKCC.

White, R. (1980) Postwar Reconstruction of Nursing. Paper presented at the RCN Research Society Conference 1980.

White, R. (1985) Political regulations in British nursing. In R. White, ed *Political Issues in Nursing: Past, Present and Future,* Vol 1. pp 19–44. London: John Wiley.

CHAPTER 7

Extending the frontiers

In the past decade, there have been two major opportunities to examine the case for the expanded role. The first was the report of the Royal Commission on the NHS, which was commissioned in May 1976 and reported in July 1979. The second was the Cumberlege Report on Community Nursing Services (1986) which reported as part of the Green Paper on Primary Health Care Services issued by the government in April 1986. The Royal Commission said:

'We think that there is considerable scope for expanding the role and responsibilities of health visitors and district nurses. As Dr Jullian MacGuire pointed out in a review of the current literature on nursing roles which she prepared for us: the involvement of nurses in screening both the very young and the elderly is already well accepted ... it is not yet routine in all practice settings for nurses to be the main contact for elderly patients ... In many cases the nurses are effectively making first contact decisions anyway though this may not always be recognised for what it is.

We consider that there are increasingly important roles for community nurses not just in the treatment room but in health surveillance for vulnerable groups and in screening procedures, health education and preventative programmes and as a point of first contact particularly for the young and the elderly.'

The Royal Commission also highlighted (page 71, para 7.3) that the extensions of these roles would increase the workload on the primary care services. They additionally noted a point about the extended role in the community which arises from the shorter times that people stay in hospitals for treatment. The nurses in the community are required to extend their role simply because people are being discharged back into the community at a much higher level of dependency.

The Royal Commission drew attention to the dissatisfaction with the services for the mentally ill in the community from the GP service. 'It is impossible to do justice to psychiatric problems within the present average consultation time of six minutes' (para 6.41).

These comments on nursing in the community have been reinforced by the findings of the Report on Community Nursing Services in England, chaired by Julia Cumberlege, the Chair of Brighton Health Authority. In her report, she claimed that her recommendations reflected what was already happening in the service in the best practices where nurses were already performing extended roles. She recommended the introduction of the nurse practitioner into the British NHS and that nurses should have extended powers of prescription for limited items where she found that they were already taking the lead. In her proposals for neighbourhood nursing services, she aimed to draw the nurse manager back into clinical practice and reverse the effect that Salmon and Mayston had had in most areas.

Her report recommended written agreements about objectives in the primary health care team, a proposal which attracted more opposition than many others since it symbolised the fact that nurses in the community would be making an agreement as equal professional partners with GPs on what services should be delivered, how they would be delivered and by whom. The recommendations of the Royal Commission were not acted upon by the incoming government in 1979; today the pressure of limited resources and the genuine demand for increased preventative measures among the population in general create a force for change which could overcome traditional obstacles.

The Royal Commission also heard evidence about the different ways in which nursing roles were being extended and expanded within the hospital with particular reference for groups such as the chronic sick and the elderly. The Regional Nursing Officers in England suggested to the Royal Commission:

'Examination should be given to the possibility of extending the role of the nurse, enabling them to undertake tasks traditionally the province of the medical staff ... There is a need in some long stay care areas for nurses to take the lead. Nurses should be enabled to prescribe nursing care programmes, including the mobilisation of other services such as physiotherapy and occupational therapy.' (13.16)

and further:

'Extended roles for nurses are developing as a result of specialisation for example in renal dialysis, care of spinal injuries and special care baby units. Advances in medical science often require parallel advances in nursing care and nurses working closely with doctors are pioneering new roles.' (13.17)

but most importantly they also recommended that: 'They will need to ensure that new developments do not take place at the expense of the nurses' caring role which is so important to patients and which is a prime candidate for expansion.'

The case for extending the frontiers of nursing was being made in the mid-1970s without the huge economic and resource pressures which now impinge on the service, yet government were reluctant to act on the recommendations because it would have involved tampering with the territory of the medical profession. This piece of political hesitation and lack of willpower is reflected further in the 1986 Green Paper on Primary Health Care Services, in which the government think aloud about whether or not we are 'realising the full potential of nurses'. This is despite the fact that the Cumberlege Report, which was published at the same time, clearly comes to the conclusion that we are not realising the full potential of nurses; and that there are clear steps which should be taken to release that potential, extending in the process the role of nursing in the primary care services.

When the World Health Organisation debated its strategy for 'Health for all by the year 2000' (Declaration of Alma Ata), it concluded that, given the tasks which were of primary importance and the financial restrictions under which many countries operated, the leading role would be taken by nursing as nursing embodies the levels of skill, in the numbers and at a price most economies could afford. This is a conclusion that the UK government has yet to confront.

The increasingly technical and specialist nature of health care since 1948 has seen the expansion of physiotherapy, radiology and the other professions now described as supplementary to medicine. In all of these, nursing has given away some ground and left the impression that there was not a key nursing dimension to these functions.

In the management reforms of the 1960s and, in particular, in the Salmon Report (1966), many of the new breed of nurse administrator effectively removed themselves from direct patient care. Salmon had intended that the nursing officer would have clinical involvement and would provide a high level of clinical nursing advice. Doctors, however, preferred to continue to relate to the ward sister and nurses moving into management did not always want to roll up their sleeves.

Outside the hospital setting, the district nursing services have been moving into a closer relationship with the GPs with more direct attachment to general practice. While they are seeing more people in their own homes and keeping the function of home nursing alive, they do so through an increasingly tight working system with GPs and the pressure of work requires them to narrow the functions they carry out. They now look to assistants with 'non-nursing duties' from a wide range of other staff, especially social services staff such as home helps. Jean McIntosh examined this well in 'District Nursing: a Case of Political Marginality' (White 1985).

The health visitors have kept a theoretical remit for initiating their own relationship with clients. In their practice, they have developed a philosophy which almost denies their nursing role in favour of their health promotion and social worker roles. When actual nursing skills, which they all have, are called upon, they tend to refer them to another part of the service—the GPs or the district nursing service. This is well documented by Jane Robinson (1985).

As the work of caring and treating has become more complex and wide ranging, we have seen greater fragmentation of tasks and functions, both within nursing and within new groups and professions such as the operating department assistants and medical social workers. There is more professional nursing available in society today than ever before but the nature of its services is becoming narrower and more specialised.

Some division of labour will always be necessary. It makes good organisational sense for the use of resources. It suits those who are practising and allows them to develop special skills to a high level. In high technology medical areas, it allows nurses to keep up with medical developments. It does, however, have a fatal flaw: patients do not divide themselves up into these neat packages. One effect of such divisions of labour is that a single patient, either in the hospital or in the community, will be handed from one professional to another as problems emerge. No one person takes an overview on behalf of the patients and clients, despite the role of ward sister, consultant and GP. A hospital ward has become a cornucopia of professional and technical skills; the home of a family needing help or support can sometimes seem like a Piccadilly Circus of the social services.

Expanding the frontiers is not just about taking on the tasks and responsibilities that the doctors no longer want or which they have overlooked. It must also look at expanding back into the areas which nursing should never have discarded. Nursing has given up so much territory to others, and while the nurse of the 80s is not exactly looking for additional responsibilities, given the pressures already on her, some fundamentals of nursing care have slipped from her and must be reclaimed.

Nursing has a wonderful ability to tie itself up in academic and abstract debate about its role while other groups simply keep their eyes fixed firmly on what is happening in the health service and make themselves essential. Lacking confidence, nurses fear entering new areas if they do not have the backing and legitimacy of academic endorsement.

Instead of looking for an all-embracing theory for expanding the frontiers of nursing, it is possible to look around the health service and see many areas which cry out for initiatives from the nursing profession. I believe nursing should target these areas in primary health care and personal care in hospital and get on with offering solutions. I believe nursing has many of the best solutions to offer and their merit will be quickly obvious. Examples of this include the work of continence advisers and stoma care nurses who have moved to fill a real gap in services to patients. The major project of the RCN's Daphne Heald research unit is to evaluate the effectiveness of such work of clinical specialists. The findings promise to be fascinating.

Outside pressures also offer opportunities. The demand from the women's movement for a more sensitive regime in the health service and demand from the public for a more holistic approach to its needs are all within the capacity of nursing to deliver.

People are seeking a wider and more informed choice. It is a demand that the nursing profession in the UK is in a position to meet better than almost any other group. I believe it can, and will, rise to this challenge.

In hospitals, the number of patients being treated is rising dramatically. The statistics, while they have their flaws, record that the number of in-patients being treated every year rose by almost 1,000,000 between 1979 and 1986. The number of day patients treated rose by 400,000 and the number of outpatients by almost 3 million. Both in hospital and in the community, the practical pressures on the medical service demand that they rely more and more heavily on nursing staff. In the GPs' service, the Royal Commission on the National Health Service (1979) recorded that the average length of time a patient could expect with a GP was six minutes. In their initial response to the Cumberlege Report (1986), the medical profession have been hostile to the ideas of an expanded role for nursing. Yet, at the same time, many doctors have been arguing for an extension of the ancillary payments scheme which would allow them to employ more nurses to relieve them of a whole range of tasks of the preventative kind identified by Cumberlege. The sheer volume of work in the traditional model of doctor-led care is forcing a re-examination which can break down barriers and shatter the territorial arguments which have been painstakingly erected by those opposed to an expanded role for nursing.

A study in Australia (Wilson and Najman, 1982) examined the extent to which nurses in hospital settings were venturing into areas which the doctors traditionally regarded as their own. These nurses were having to undertake the work and their medical colleagues were sanctioning it, regardless of the legal position or the rules imposed by senior nurses.

At present, we have a sickness service in which the GPs act as the gatekeepers for the hospitals and deal with a wide range of minor illnesses. Each day, 30,000 GPs see approximately 650,000 people who are, or believe they are, sick. The government now states in its 1986 Green Paper on Primary Health Care that it wants to see a primary health care service where people receive a wider range of services to help them promote health and prevent illness. It wishes to see the health service monitor its local population and provide services for people at key points in their lives when counselling, screening, advice and health promotion work could make considerable differences. This is not high technology; the level of skill required does not need a medical training, and much of the work does not involve the traditional preserve of the doctor. In terms of sheer volume it presents a considerable challenge and doctors have inevitably begun to use nursing staff in an extended role. It is not uncommon to find that in a group practice screening for cervical cancer will be undertaken by the nursing staff; the same is true for many of the other preventative tasks which are in theory undertaken by the doctor.

The trend of delegating non-nursing duties requires re-examination. Pressure is also mounting for nursing to reconsider its role and to reclaim some of the 'non-nursing duties' which nurses in the past were too ready to give away. When a person comes into hospital, they enter an alien and threatening environment. They may be in for a relatively simple surgical procedure, but the patient may greatly fear the personal humiliations associated with it. The most basic, but vital, tasks like toileting and feeding can assume massive significance for a patient who has spent her or his whole adult life completely independent and competent. The psychological scars which are often left after a visit to the operating theatre can go deeper than the physical effects. For patients with strokes, every routine daily chore becomes important and often excruciating. These things are vital because they contribute to the patient's recovery, peace of mind, or state of dignity. As a more holistic approach is demanded by the public and the right to more informed choice and the preservation of individual dignity take higher priority, there will be many more instances where the nursing staff who have the information and the broader view must ask themselves questions about the rigid delegation of non-nursing duties to untrained staff.

The work of Alison Kitson on what makes a therapeutic nurse challenges nursing to reconsider some of the tasks it has shed over the years. Many jobs will still be done by people not trained in nursing; however, in taking an overview of the needs of the individual, nurses will continue, on many occasions, to undertake these tasks in order to respond to the demand for a more holistic and sensitive approach to health care which respects the dignity of the individual and promotes recovery.

The central preoccupation of health planners is the growing number of elderly people and how their needs will be met by the health service. Both the growing number and the stated policy of caring for as many as possible in the community stretches all services to their limit. Already nurses in the community are maintaining many people independently and the participation of the medical profession amounts to little more than a rubber stamp.

In the private sector, the early 1980s have seen a phenomenal growth in private residential homes and nursing homes for the elderly. Many of these developments have been led by nurses. Not for the first time, a development in the private sector has allowed nurses more scope to develop services and to take a leadership role than they can find in the state system with its entrenched territorial disputes.

For most elderly people, the issue really is one of care where there is no cure and of maintaining the quality of life for themselves and for their families for as long as possible. Nursing's contribution must go beyond simply caring for those whose health has gone into decline; it must offer the prospect of reaching people in their late middle age and persuading them about lifestyles and health promotion measures which will enable them to remain fitter for longer. Health visiting has not achieved the contact with the elderly population which makes this possible, so other nurses in the community shoulder much of the increasing burden.

Promotion and prevention programmes which are at present dependent on people coming to the health service could be improved if nursing staff, monitoring a population, were given more scope to take precautions and initiate action, as, for example, health visitors track down children who have not been immunised.

Nurses already carry out screening programmes for breast and cervical cancers. The fact that the majority of nurses are women is relevant when considering how best to get women to come forward and use the service. Many of the skills required for family planning services, contraceptive advice and sexual counselling are well within the competence of family planning nurses, but they still cannot prescribe the Pill.

It is estimated that as many as 30 per cent of those who present themselves at GPs' surgeries have a psychological problem or need counselling in some way. With doctors only able to give a limited amount of time, this is an area where community psychiatric nurses play a vital role. One of the most consistent complaints about visits to the GP's surgery is that the doctor never seems to be able to give enough time. In the Cumberlege Report, a survey of public opinion on community health care found that almost two-thirds of patients would be happy to see a nurse, rather than a doctor, for a specific purpose. Many of these purposes would fall into the categories set out above.

One of the most underdeveloped areas in primary health care is the health provision for the working population at their place of work. Occupational health nursing has been severely neglected, yet much illness and disease, as well as accidents, are caused by work. We spend almost half our waking hours at work. A holistic approach, taking account of both physical well-being and the inevitable stresses of life and work, has the potential to do much for the health of the nation.

In the last 20 years, nursing has followed medical specialisation into such areas as oncology and rheumatology. There is little dispute about the role that nurses have to play in such situations. I am concerned, however, that in going into these specialist roles, nurses should be expanding their role around the needs of the patient and client rather than simply relieving doctors of work that they do not have the time or the inclination to do. Nurses might do it better.

Another setting for the development of a wider role for nursing staff is in the Accident and Emergency Department. The tradition that every casualty must be seen by a doctor places great stress on the medical staff and makes for lengthy waiting times; understandably people become angry and frustrated. It was estimated at Old Church Hospital in Romford, Essex, that of the 100,000 people who passed through the Accident and Emergency doors each year almost 25 per cent could have been dealt with, or referred back to their GP, by the nursing sisters and charge nurses in the unit. When such a scheme was announced, doctors' representatives appeared on television to express grave doubts about the principle, while many of their colleagues were screaming out for any system which would relieve their workload.

In all these areas the medical profession and critics of the nursing profession continually raise the question of competence. Are the nurses competent to make an assessment of the patient and will it be the correct assessment? Will they miss anything? The Royal Commission noted that in *The Lancet* (Royal Commission on the NHS 1979) and Moore *et al.* (1973) as long ago as 1973 an experiment carried out at the Woodside Health Centre in Glasgow showed that 'the decisions made independently by nurses and doctors about what to do for patients in the community were very similar'.

Since that time further studies (including the work of Stillwell in Birmingham) have been carried out, in this country and elsewhere, which confirm that nurses are competent to carry out first contacts with patients, and to recognise problems which require diagnosis from a medical practitioner.

Community psychiatric nurses would confirm that there are significant gaps in the training of GPs about psychiatric problems and that too many GPs have resorted to prescribing drugs, such as Valium, when counselling and other help and time was really required.

Such extended roles for nurses are well established in other countries, most notably in the case of the nurse practitioner in parts of the USA and the public health nurse in countries like Finland. The question of competence has been faced in those countries. In this country the work of Barbara Stillwell, a nurse practitioner in inner-city Birmingham, has received much publicity and praise, in particular her work with ethnic minorities, especially Asian women. In the USA, the nurse practitioners have taken a front-line role in the poor and rural areas where it is difficult to get doctors to practice, but they play a role in the hospital setting too. It is a role that can, I believe, be provided throughout the health service, not just in those gaps which the medical profession has left.

There is an urgent need to look at ways in which the resources which go to the care teams, whether in hospital or in the community, can be better distributed to give people the type of service they want and need. A better use of nurses in an expanded role would achieve much of this. The object is not to create a new breed of elitist nurses pursuing the glamour of closer association with the frontiers of medical technology (in some areas that already exists in specialist nursing) but to expand nursing skills into areas where they can be most effective and where the demand is best and most economically met by nursing rather than medical skills.

In this development, nursing education has part of the solution but it is also part of the problem. I believe that the extended role already practised by many nurses should be recognised and confirmed, and the necessary education and training provided, for the extended role needs to become consolidated and fully accepted. The reaction of some nurse educationists is to join the chorus of those who say that the nurse is working beyond her/his competence.

Traditional nurse training and education has reflected this rigidity and inflexibility. It has contributed to the argument that nurses should shed non-nursing duties and to the strict definition of roles. Nursing has been analysed as a series of tasks and functions and the education programmes have been prepared to give nurses a training based on that analysis. While the arrival of the nursing process and individualised patient care has changed some thinking, we have not really taught student nurses to think in the flexible way that would enable them to get the greatest benefit from such new approaches. As a system of individualised care the nursing process applied by people trained in the routine and ritual of British nursing was bound to run into problems. Ideas like the nursing process as an extension of the nursing role have often foundered on the very ritual and routine of nursing which they were meant to replace.

If the nursing profession in the UK is to undertake an extended role then it will have to shed some of its rigid approaches to work. It will have to look at each individual's circumstances and at the resources available and how these can best be mobilised for effective delivery of care. To bow to limited resources may seem like sacrilege, but to carry on with a prescription for care which will founder on the limited resources available is also to betray the patients. There is a nursing shortage in the UK but the sense of the shortage for individual nurses is made even worse by the rigid structure within which they have to work. It gives them a constant sense of failure and a feeling of never being able to do things properly. An extended role and better education for that role could transform the situation and allow for a more flexible and satisfying response.

While much work has been going on in these areas, it remains a scandal that the potential contribution of the largest single group of people working in the NHS, the nursing staff, has so little resources committed to it for research. The government commits hundreds of millions of pounds to medical research while potentially huge improvements in the delivery of care struggle for recognition. Many managers regard nurse staffing levels as essentially a personnel problem. Careful judgements of grade and skill mix are relegated in favour of crude studies of staffing comparisons between wards. Research which examined the possibility of large areas of health care being competently undertaken by nursing staff would represent a fundamental rethink.

Research into improving the usage of nursing staff could give policy makers new options in the search for more affordable means of delivering primary health care, for faster and more sensitive treatment in hospitals, and for better information and counselling for patients, to name but a few areas that need research work.

If there is to be an extended role for nursing, which the combination of pressures within the health care service and from economic pressures outside would seem to demand, then I believe that it has to go much further than simply following the medical profession into greater specialisation, high technology and new drugs. Nursing must expand back into areas which it has lost, it must bring the priority of caring for the whole individual back into many hospitals which treat people so intensively for such short periods of time. Nursing must reclaim those domestic and personal tasks which may appear routine but assume a psychological importance in the recovery of the patient and have a key therapeutic value. Nurses in the community must be given the right to be the first point of contact; it is a necessary development and one which many people have indicated they wish to have. Nurse managers, too, will have to return to the clinical area if they are to contribute to leading a service where nurses act more independently and to a higher level of competence. Extending the frontiers is about offering new services and about tackling the tendency the nursing profession has displayed for decades to narrow its own remit by a rigid view of what constitutes nursing duties. Such an approach will command public support and be irresistible politically.

Nursing has demonstrated its potential, therefore, in many key areas. Instead of continuing the search for the Holy Grail of abstract academic legitimacy, we must now act clearly, decisively and urgently.

Rather than look for a grand philosophy for the parameters of nursing, I believe it is important to look at the areas where nurses are playing an extended role, to develop that role and consolidate it.

The three key areas where changes need to be taken forward are:

Prevention and promotion of health

With the very young, with the elderly, through immunisation programmes, family planning, cancer screening, psychological counselling and occupational health.

Treatment

Of the chronically sick and the disabled, through psychiatric work in the community and dispensing limited prescriptions, in casualty departments, renal care, orthopedic nursing, paediatric nursing, stoma care, diabetes, incontinence and a wide range of other recognised nursing specialties.

Attitude changes

1. Recognise the therapeutic function of many 'non nursing' duties and recognise when they have to be reclaimed by nurses.
2. Nurse managers have to re-establish their clinical involvement.
3. Nurse specialisation must avoid simply following medical priorities or the drive towards technology.

References

McIntosh, J. (1985). District nursing: a case of political marginality. In White (ed.). *Political Issues in Nursing: Past Present and Future*. Vol. 1. London: John Wiley & Sons.

Moore *et al.* (1973) First contact decisions in general practice. *Lancet*, April 14.

Neighbourhood Nursing: a focus for care (Cumberlege Report) (1986) The Community Nursing Review, London: HMSO.

Report of the Committee on Senior Nursing Staff Structure (Salmon Report) (1966) London: HMSO.

Robinson, J. (1985) Health visiting and health. In R. White (ed.) *Political Issues in Nursing: Past Present and Future*. Vol. 1. London: John Wiley & Sons.

Royal Commission on the NHS (1979) London: HMSO.

Wilson, D. A. J. and Najman, J. M. (1982) After Nightingale: a preliminary report of work undertaken by nurses in Queensland. *Journal of Australian Nurses* 4, October.

World Health Organisation (1978) *Declaration of Alma Ata*. Geneva: WHO.

CHAPTER 8

The real work of nurses

Since when have the working practices of nurses been political? The changed climate came in the summer of 1983 when the College was gathering information from its members about the effects of financial cutbacks in services in the NHS with the highly successful *Nurse Alert* campaign. Perhaps fearing that the information would be politically damaging, the government pre-empted the report and turned to scrutinise nurses at work. It became fashionable for Conservative MPs to say: 'Do you know that in my local hospital, there is four-hour overlap in nursing shifts during the afternoon? What industry would allow that kind of extravagance?'

So unused was the profession to scrutiny from outside that, it must be admitted, our response was neither swift nor convincing. First there was the shock of realising that the hallowed walls had been breached. Then there was the horror of discovering that some places clearly did have a four-hour overlap, which nurses could not justify. Finally, there came a torrent of explanation and justification so frenzied that it only served to underline our vulnerability. Rather belatedly, Mary Armstrong, an RCN Council member, wrote a clear article in *Nursing Times* explaining the reasons for the shift overlap. This was reprinted in the *Nurse Alert* report (1984).

That summer, the Minister for Health, Kenneth Clarke, never one to shy away from controversy, said in a radio interview that in some areas of nursing overmanning existed. At the time manpower targets were being set for each region, and included in some places substantial reductions in nursing posts. The effect on the profession was electrifying. How could he say such a thing? Everyone knows how short of staff our hospital and community services are. Let him come and see my ward.

But unfortunately the climate was changing. Righteous indignation was no longer enough. Mrs Thatcher's government had just been returned with a resounding majority of 140, and was pledged to bring efficiency and cost-effectiveness to the public services, most notably to the NHS. A new political era had arrived and the new political scrutineers were not to be fobbed off with superficial reassurances, incoherent anger or pseudo-scientific answers. Expenditure on nursing and midwifery is big business: it uses up 34 per cent of the NHS's total revenue budget and accounts for almost £3 in every £100 that Mrs Thatcher spends.

So was nursing overmanned? Despite hundreds of patient dependency studies and related work carried out throughout the UK and brought together by the DHSS (1982 and 1983), and despite the fairly widespread use of manpower schemes such as the Aberdeen formula, the truth is that we do not know much about how many nurses—and of what kind—are 'needed' (Miller 1984). And the government did not take long to spot this Achilles' heel. The subsequent inquiries into nursing manpower by the National Audit Office, the Public Accounts Committee and most recently the NHS Management Board's Skill Mix Review are signposts on the same political pathway that Kenneth Clarke mapped out in that triumphant summer of 1983.

In this chapter, I intend to argue the case for a fully qualified nursing workforce in our hospital and community services. This may initially appear to be flying in the face of political reality, with the mounting nurse manpower crisis in the NHS, increasing demand for nursing care, and continual, relentless pressure on general managers to deliver the goods on efficiency savings. But I believe that as a longer-term goal it is the profession's duty to society to pursue this, however difficult it proves to be. As one of our members wrote in her comments on UKCC's Project 2000: 'Our patients have a moral right to be cared for by qualified nurses.' Another wrote: 'We must not be guided by what we think politicians will accept—we must set our goals high and propose a qualified nursing service.' I intend to argue the case by explaining the injustices to both nurses and patients in the existing 'system' and to show how a fully qualified nursing workforce would ultimately be a more efficient and effective way of delivering care.

Political Scrutiny

To set the scene politically I will look first at those three recent reports on nursing manpower, and what they have meant for the profession.

Virtually out of the blue in the summer of 1985 came a short, lucid report from the Comptroller and Auditor General of the National Audit Office which examined the control of nursing manpower in the NHS. This set out to find the truth behind the increase in nursing staff between 1976 and 1983 (from 342,000 to 397,000 WTEs) and to explore whether nursing manpower was being used in the most 'efficient and effective' manner. The report mentioned that in 1969 the Committee of Public Accounts was concerned that health departments did not know whether there were too many or too few nurses—20 years after the NHS came into being.

On the positive side for nursing, the report contained the best 'official' explanation yet as to why the numbers of nursing staff increased by 16 per cent between 1976 and 1983. The reduction of the working week accounted for nearly half the growth and the rest was 'at least partly justified because of increased demands for health care and improvement in nursing staffing levels in the priority specialties of mental illness and geriatrics'. But, it added, inadequate information systems make it difficult to discover whether the increases were fully justified. Health authorities were urged to do better. This explanation is important because the increase in numbers of nursing staff is frequently cited as a feather in the government's cap. As Norman Fowler, Secretary of State for Social Services, restated at the 1986 Conservative Party Conference in Bournemouth: 'More doctors and more nurses are working for patients than at any stage in the history of the health service. They were providing more and better patient care—four and a half million more cases are being treated today than when we came to office.'

It may seem churlish constantly to remind the public of the reasons for these increases, but it *is* possible for 55,000 nurses to be virtually swallowed up in a service as vast as the NHS without an appreciable improvement in the quality of patient care.

The report dissected several manpower-related practices and suggested ideas for economies, for example in reducing the overlap to no longer than 90 minutes. On the question of determining manpower requirements, the NAO recognised that no single methodology was perfect but that nurse managers should use their skill and experience in conjunction with dependency studies. It also looked ahead to the day when performance indicators would show up health authorities which still had not got their manpower 'right'.

The College's magazine *Lampada* (1985) commented at the time on the dangers for nursing in the view that if a ward is apparently coping with staffing levels below the norm, this was proof that it could be done. In 40 per cent of cases the NAO found that the use of one of the accepted formulae for determining staffing levels gave a figure higher than the funded establishment and considerably more than the number of staff in post. The DHSS told the Audit Office that this showed that 'under pressure of resource constraints, authorities managed with something a little less than what various methodologies would suggest ... without serious adverse effects on patient care.' *Lampada* urged readers to refute this if it happened to them locally. The report predicted that savings could also be made by 'rationalising' the mix and deployment of nursing skills. One authority, it was estimated, would save £378,000 by changing the mix of grades, including a reduction in the number of sisters.

In February 1986, the House of Commons Committee of Public Accounts published its report on nursing manpower, having examined the NAO's findings—and received a paper from the RCN. The Committee obviously relished the fact that the DHSS still did not have the information to enable them to say whether there were too many or too few nurses employed in the NHS. It also commented that if the DHSS really considered central manpower control to be 'impractical' it was surprising that in 1983 reductions were imposed from the centre, precipitating a drop in nursing numbers.

It still seems odd to me to see the working practices of nurses examined in a parliamentary report of this kind. The temptation to say that it is none of their business is almost irresistible, but the expenditure implications of the nursing workforce of course makes it a matter of public concern. The RCN, however, did succeed in shifting the ground on the manpower debate from the underlying political question, 'How can the service do more with less?' to 'Where are the nurses of the future coming from?'

The research carried out for the College's Commission on Nursing Education (1985) highlighted the prospect of an imminent shortage of nurses as the supply of suitably qualified school-leavers declined, the demand for nursing care increased, and if the present training system with its 35 per cent drop-out rate were allowed to continue. The Royal College of Nursing fed this information to the Committee, who recorded their view that this was 'a most serious matter of direct importance to patients'. The Department was urged to move into action straight away to avert the impending manpower crisis.

Overall, the Committee endorsed the NAO's recommendations and put the onus on the newly installed general managers to use performance indicators and other such tools to put their nursing house in order. All the signs are that their work on this most diffi-cult area is being overtaken by events, so that the problem is not so much who one recruits to do what on the ward, but whether one can recruit anyone at all.

The long-awaited nursing skill mix review (Mix and Match 1986) arrived without much publicity in June 1986. Alongside the report, Len Peach, then acting Chairman of the NHS Manage-ment Board, urged general managers to give the better deploy-ment of nursing staff a high priority and to act immediately on the cumulative message of the three manpower reports.

The study focusing on the areas of long-stay mentally ill, mentally handicapped, elderly people, high dependency and in-tensive care, was carried out in eight districts over two weeks. Unsurprisingly it revealed enormous variation from place to place in the range of qualifications, the proportion of qualified to unqualified, and overall staffing levels. It urges health authorities to start work on finding out the most appropriate skill mix and target ratios. It also found that the roles of staff and enrolled nurses were regarded as interchangeable and that gaps in the support services were covered up by nurses. On long-stay wards which had students in training the level of qualified nurses was often lower than in other wards.

I have two particular worries about this report, based on im-plicit rather than explicit suggestions. First, there is the impli-cation that managerial virtue consists of diluting the qualified nursing workforce as much as is safe to do so. The 'skill mix' is really—and the report admits this—'grade and qualification mix'; it seems that managers are being urged to pursue the lowest common denominator to compile a nursing workforce

which is the cheapest consistent with minimum standards of care
and safety. Some would say this is simply good management. But
the arguments in favour of the utilisation of qualified nurses must
be heard and heeded. NHS management can never be effective as
long as arguments about quantity carry more weight than those
about quality.

The second concern I have is the implication that this debate
about nursing manpower can be had by swapping formulae,
devising ever more intricate ratios and by relying on pseudo-
scientific reasoning. Of course the nursing profession has relied
too much in the past on routine and tradition ('It's got to be like
that, because it has always been like that') and not made proper
use of the research and the lessons from practical experience that
exist. But a computer print-out based on all the facts and figures,
ratios and formulae in the world could never replace the skill, experience and professional knowledge of a nurse manager in
making crucial decisions about deployment of staff.

It becomes vital, therefore, for general managers to use nurse
managers in the work they must now be carrying out on manpower. And it also becomes vital for nursing managers at every
level from regional nursing officer to ward sister to be aware of
these discussions and be prepared to play a full part in them, to
come forward without being asked if necessary. In the new
managerial climate, it is definitely not fashionable to say that the
opinion of a ward sister about how many nurses she needs on her
ward and how many students and auxiliaries she can adequately
supervise counts for more than any scientific formula. But it
probably does.

These three reports together, therefore, amount to an unprecedented level of scrutiny of the nursing workforce, which has hit
the profession at a time when its managers are, at worst, absent
or devoid of any real power or influence, and at best taking on
unfamiliar responsibilities or uncertain about new managerial
relationships. The arrival of general management, whatever its
value, has hit the nursing profession for six. Nursing has invested
a great deal over the years in training its managers for leadership
positions, and a cadre of potential leaders was being built up. The
advent of general management has set this back at least two
decades.

Against this background, how will it be possible to win the
argument for a wholly qualified nursing workforce? The soil, I

admit, does not at first glance look fertile, but a strong case can be made on the grounds both of quality of care and of economics. First, let us look at the shortcomings of the present system, in which nursing auxiliaries, student nurses and enrolled nurses are all in different ways misused and exploited.

The Auxiliaries

The number of nursing auxiliaries has grown steadily, from 108,000 in 1979 to 114,000 in 1985. They now form 24 per cent of the workforce, compared with students and pupils (17 per cent) and qualified staff (59 per cent).

No-one doubts their importance in helping to keep the service running, and in many places they are valuable and experienced members of the ward team. Yet the shortage of qualified staff often means that auxiliaries are carrying out their work without either adequate supervision or proper training for the responsibilities they are forced to shoulder. Nursing has preferred to turn a blind eye to this state of affairs in its research priorities with the notable exception of Hardie (1978), who found that all the major tasks of qualified nurses were being carried out by auxiliaries. With a group forming 25 per cent of the workforce we also conveniently overlook the inevitability of students 'learning' from auxiliaries at least as much as they 'learn' from qualified staff:

'Consider the factual differences between the work of the student nurse, pupil nurse and the nursing auxiliary: carrying out the same work, at the same time with the same patients. Only the looming examinations make the difference, in addition to the relative permanence of the auxiliary as against the instability of the learner.' (Hardie 1983)

This ambivalence, not to say hypocrisy, manifests itself in the question of the training of auxiliaries. It is plainly wrong from both the patients' and the staffs' point of view that people can virtually walk in off the streets to work closely with extremely sick or dependent patients in the ward setting. Yet this is often precisely what happens—with any form of training or even induction being comparatively rare. Authorities which do provide training tend not to boast about it, and nurse managers have not been quick to promote it in case they are thought to be vesting in auxiliaries a professional standing which they clearly do not have.

The political history of nursing this century is dominated by successive attempts to solve the manpower crisis in nursing by opening new doors. Able-Smith (1960) describes how in the 1930s the increasing use of ward orderlies led to the development of assistant nurses. By the outbreak of the Second World War, the Athlone Committee's proposals (1938) to open 'the second portal' had been accepted. There was to be a two-year training and enrolment for 'girls with a practical bent for nursing but without the intellectual equipment necessary' for state registration. The Nurses Act of 1943, under wartime pressures, opened up the Roll and most existing assistant nurses were 'grandfathered', i.e. absorbed on to the Roll without further training or examination.

The shortages were not solved by this; by 1958 the number of 'other nursing staff' was 50 per cent higher than the number of enrolled nurses. A third portal was partially opened and the nursing auxiliary took up her uneasy position alongside qualified nurses. The profession is soundly rebuked by Able-Smith for being so unrealistic about the manpower crisis. 'Either the profession had to delegate part of the care of the patient to less skilled persons provided with such training as they would absorb or else it had to alter the requirements for state registration.'

The College's Commission on Nurse Education (1985) did not directly address the issue of nursing auxiliaries, although their ghosts haunt the chapter on manpower and cost implications. The Centre of Health Economics' work suggest that 20,000 extra staff would be needed to replace the lost student and pupil contribution. It is argued that this could be spread over a number of years, giving a shortfall of 2,000–4,000 WTE per annum compared to an estimated shortfall of 12,000–15,000 per annum if the present wasteful system is allowed to continue. However optimistic one is about who these staff are going to be—and I remain ever optimistic—the task of searching out sufficient qualified nurses is clearly going to be exceedingly difficult. The nursing auxiliary in some form or another will be here for some time to come.

By largely ignoring the issue, the RCN's Commission received very few questions about the future of the auxiliary. Project 2000 (1986), on the other hand, took the bull firmly by the horns and 'noted' the views of those who said that 'strictly speaking Council had no locus of responsibility in relation to anyone but the registered practitioner'. The Project proposed that a new helper grade should be introduced, to whom the practitioner would assign work. For this the helper, for whom the title 'aide' is proposed, would receive in-service instruction over a period of three months, arranged by the employing authority based on guidelines from the National Boards.

In an ideal world, says Project 2000, 'most would wish to see registered practitioners giving all the care needed'. Unfortunately, I believe it would take an equally ideal world to ensure that the aide is only used in the carefully circumscribed ways that are proposed.

The Enrolled Nurses

Now we turn to the enrolled nurse, whose position is at least as difficult as the auxiliary and as much open to abuse, misunderstanding and inconsistency. At one moment, the EN is one of the ward's lowliest beings, at everyone's beck and call and carrying responsibility without authority, the next that same nurse is called upon to run the ward because the grade mix has changed and she or he becomes top dog. It is little wonder enrolled nurses feel dissatisfied with this see-saw.

The enrolled nurse grade also represents one of the health service's biggest confidence tricks. Pupil nurse courses were filled in the 1950s and 1960s by recruits from Mauritius, the Phillipines and elsewhere, who were misled into believing they were doing a registered nurse training that would put them on a secure career path. Too late they discovered that the enrolled nurse qualification is the road to nowhere in the UK, and virtually useless back home. Even now this con trick goes on, with some careers teachers guiding school-leavers into pupil nurse training on the grounds that you get in two years what student nurses get in three. Fortunately, schools of nursing are getting the message and either scrapping pupil nurse training or reducing the intakes as shown in the most recent figures, down to 7,650 in 1986 from 24,800 in 1982.

More conversion courses are always proposed as the solution to the EN 'problem'. But as Project 2000 reluctantly recognised, the substantial extra resources for adequate courses are unlikely to be available—and the buck was passed to the National Boards. On this tricky question, the RCN Council, at the instigation of the enrolled nurse advisory group, has taken some courageous decisions and agreed a policy of grandfathering. This would give enrolled nurses a choice:

- to transfer to first level qualification after three years' practice, subject to proof of competence,

- or to be trained in first level specialist nursing if they are already trained at enrolled level in that specialty,

- or to remain at EN level and to be protected for the remainder of their employment.

I believe this is the right course, and that compromise is not possible. Nursing requires a certain level of intelligence, skill and knowledge; it is a complex operation in which the so-called 'basic' and 'routine' part cannot be separated from the rest. Professor Jean McFarlane has long fought for the abolition of the phrase 'basic nursing care' and I support her in this battle. If one accepts this, it is illogical to go along with the notion of different levels. The pace of life on wards and in the community is now such that the notion of qualified nurses adequately supervising, teaching and monitoring the work of the less qualified or unqualified is totally unrealistic. Such a separation of work and responsibility is not viable, and we should recognise this as soon as possible. I believe this is a realistic and honest view. The parallels drawn in the 1950s (*Nursing Times* 1955) between care of a sick person at home being carried out by an untrained relative and the utilisation of someone less qualified than a registered nurse to do 'basic' nursing in hospital are now totally outdated. Patients in acute hospitals in the 1980s are admitted for much shorter periods in which they are usually very sick and dependent. The health economics of the 1980s mean that no-one is allowed to occupy a hospital bed longer than is strictly necessary. There are no convalescents and very few extended periods for 'observation and rest'. In the USA with the introduction of DRGs (diagnostic-related groups) hospital stays are tightly financially controlled through the reimbusement system and the effect on the mix of patients in hospitals has been dramatic.

The hospital of the 1980s is no place for demarcation disputes between different grades of nurse. I do not believe it will ever be possible to devise a satisfactory and workable system of dividing up nursing care into what a registered nurse can do and what an enrolled nurse can do. Any system, no matter how research-based or managerially analysed, would break down instantly under the pressure and pace of life on the wards and the second level nurse would continue, as today, to feel misused and exploited.

The third component in the nursing pie-chart is students, now constituting 17 per cent of the workforce. The need for students to be supernumerary, proposed as long ago as 1943 in the Horder Report, is now very widely acknowledged. This proposal was a cornerstone of both the Judge Report and Project 2000 and is discussed more fully in Chapter 6.

The Manpower Monster

Professor Able-Smith has charted the key periods in nursing's history when the manpower monster compelled the government to act. This was always with the profession's agreement, albeit reluctant, as the pressures of expediency pushed out longer term and ultimately more sensible policies. We are now facing another of those key moments of decision in which the twin debates about manpower and education are in full voice.

Ultimately it will be about the choice between, on one hand, short-term solutions (or attempted solutions) and protecting certain vested interests and, on the other, a longer-term solution and challenging those interests. The creation of a wholly qualified workforce will only come about when nursing is able to attract and retain sufficient people, and that will only happen when students are working towards an academically credible qualification and all nurses work in an environment that enables them to nurse at something like the standard they aspire to. Improved pay is inevitably a component of this.

Where is my evidence? In this country little work has been done on the financial and qualitative benefits of a qualified workforce. The notable exception is Burford (Pearson 1985) where a small cottage hospital has moved successfully to a system of primary nursing. The critics, of course, say that a 12-bed hospital gives no indication of how well such a system would work in a larger, more complex setting. Oxford Health Authority is therefore replicating the study at a ward at the Radcliffe Infirmary, where a number of Burford experiments are being tried.

As shown in Chapter 5, creative thinking about how clinical nursing is structured has had little opportunity ever to get past the blueprint stage. Alan Pearson's excellent book, *The Clinical Nursing Unit*, shows how the several decades of research on both sides of the Atlantic could form the basis of a new kind of organisation of nursing care, using a modified system of primary nursing, research-based practice, and testing for quality. Pearson sweeps away all thinking which runs, 'That won't work because we've never done it, it'll cost too much, we tried it once and it failed, we haven't got the staff ...'

The results from Oxford will be important and fascinating in the quest for a qualified nursing service. Sue Pembrey, holding an interesting post in clinical practice development in Oxford, has done much to create the milieu in which the Burford experiment has flourished. She has perhaps been nursing's most eloquent advocate of a qualified nursing service, believing it to be the single most important commitment.

> 'The way in which we organise nursing does not promote the belief that qualified nurses should nurse patients. We have rag-bag teams of registered and enrolled nurses, students, pupils and auxiliaries and no clear, individual and consistent role for qualified nurses. Many staff nurses, who should view their role as an ideal one in which to nurse patients, instead see it as a temporary necessity to becoming a sister and being in charge.'
> (Pembrey 1984)

The other hospital in Britain which is proving that a qualified workforce can be at least as cost-effective as a mixed team is the Royal Marsden Hospital in London. This is also accused of being atypical—a privileged post-graduate hospital, which has no basic nursing students. But the Marsden achievement is considerable, not least in creating a nursing milieu which is challenging, satisfying and attractive to staff. If shortage of qualified staff is cited as the reason for the continued use of student and untrained labour, then other hospitals could well examine the techniques the Marsden has used to create an environment where nurses want to nurse because when they get there, they are able to give the standard of care they aspire to, rather than attempt to supervise and organise nursing in an unsatisfactory way (Tiffany 1984).

When the chips are down in this current manpower and education debate, I would rather opt to retain a controlled number of auxiliaries, trained to do specific tasks under the supervision of the registered nurse, than to retain a second-level nurse. If this means closing the second portal and opening the third, then so be it. And if this means that supernumerary status for students becomes achievable, this compromise would be worthwhile. We have learnt a double lesson: that short-term solutions in the interests of expediency are no solutions at all, and that if we cannot agree a longer-term strategy, the government's scruntineers will propose one for us.

Finally, here are ten pointers towards achieving a fully qualified nursing workforce by means of a better use of the staff we already have. These measures, which can mostly be achieved by good management, are not the sole answer, but would make at least some inroads into the imminent manpower crisis.

1. Make use of the tools that already exist to assess the number of nurses actually required in different parts of the service.
2. Use this to ensure no nursing time is 'wasted', painful though this might be.
3. Iron out inequalities between units so that distribution of resources is as fair as possible.
4. Treat with care and attention nurses who show interest in returning to the service—many are put off by inhospitable attitudes.
5. Be more imaginative in the way school children and local students are presented with the possibility of a career in nursing.
6. Use part-timers more usefully and effectively by matching their use to the realities of the in-patient's day—or begin to change the in-patient's day to make it less gruelling.
7. Work out areas where flexible working is acceptable and devise a system that is both workable for staff and appropriate to the service.
8. Find out about the holiday arrangements of medical staff, especially surgeons, and take this into account in allocating annual leave to nurses.
9. Much more regard should be paid to the nursing consequences of additional consultant posts: they are almost always significant.

10. Keep careful track of changes—even apparently minor ones—in medical policy. These can have a dramatic effect on standards of care unless the nursing aspects are considered.

References

Able-Smith, B. (1960) *A History of the Nursing Profession*. London: Heinemann Educational Books.

Department of Health and Social Security, Operational Research Service (1983) *Nurse Manpower Planning: Approaches and Techniques*. London: HMSO.

Department of Health and Social Security (1982) *Maintaining the Balance*. London: HMSO.

Hardie, M. (1978, 1979, 1980) *The Auxiliaries Studies*. Nursing Research Unit, University of Edinburgh.

Hardie, M. (1983) A case of professional neglect. *Nursing Times*, July 13.

House of Commons Committee of Public Accounts (1986) *Control of Nursing Manpower*. London: HMSO.

Interim Report of the Inter-departmental Committee on Nursing Services (Athlone) (1938) London: Ministry of Health.

Judge Commission on Nursing Education (1985) *The Education of Nurses: A New Dispensation*. London: RCN.

Lampada (1985) Leading article, Issue no 5, Autumn. London: RCN.

Miller, A. (1984) Does Dependency Count? *Senior Nurse*, 1 (29): 10–11.

Mix and Match, A Review of nursing skill mix (1986) NHS Management Board. London: HMSO.

Nursing Times (1955) Leading article, June 17, p. 659.

Pearson, A. (1984) The Burford Experience. *Nursing Mirror* 159 (22): 32–35.

Pearson, A. (1983) *The Clinical Nursing Unit*. London: Heinemann Medical Books.

Pembrey, S. (1984) In praise of competence: extract from 1984 Kathleen Raven Lecture. *Lampada*, Autumn 1984. London: RCN.

Report by the Comptroller and Auditor General (1985) *NHS: Control of Nursing Manpower*. London: HMSO.

Royal College of Nursing (1984) *Nurse Alert*. London: RCN

Royal College of Nursing (1986) *Evidence to the Review Body for Nursing Staff, Midwives and Health Visitors and Professions allied to Medicine*. London: RCN.

Tiffany, R. (1984) The Marsden Experience. *Nursing Mirror* 159 (22).

United Kingdom Central Council for Nursing, Midwifery and Health Visitors (1986) *Project 2000: A New Preparation for Practice*. London: UKCC.

CHAPTER 9

Image, culture and women

As a man leading a predominantly female organisation, I am often surprised by the apparent nonchalance with which women accept male leadership of the profession. I say 'apparent' because beneath the surface I know many women are far from content with this imbalance and would like to find ways of changing it. I believe the time has come to open up this issue and to stop shying away from a situation which is often side-stepped because it raises uncomfortable notions of feminism and, dare one say it, lust for power.

Why should these notions be uncomfortable? 'Power' is beginning to slip more easily into nursing parlance as nurses realise that it need not always have connotations of manipulation, abuse, or exploitation. But a discussion of the relationship between feminist theory and nursing is still unusual and the tide of the women's movement, in Britain at least, has largely passed nursing by. This is all the more remarkable when one considers how fertile the ground has become, with more articulate and questioning recruits into the profession, a greater self-confidence in clinical practice, shown by individualised patient care and acceptance of accountability, with men dominating the top positions in nursing, and doctors—male and female—protecting the medical model and reinforcing their 'male' stereotype.

But the seeds still largely lie dormant and male hegemony rolls on. The introduction of general management, which has dislodged and in many places destroyed the nursing hierarchies, has knocked many female nursing managers out of the scene and created an NHS management with an overwhelming male ethos. When Nuttall (1983) asked 'Male takeover or female giveaway?', she found 43.8 per cent of DNO positions and 50.5 per cent of DNEs held by men. Once all the new general managers are in post, it will be worth calculating how many nurses who have become general managers are men and how many female nurse managers are left in influential positions. I suspect a high proportion of nursing general managers are men and we already know that very few of the female general managers are nurses.

This means that general management has been a step backwards not only for nurses in the NHS, but for women generally. As recently as January 1985, it was possible to find women at every level of the NHS. Women were firmly at the top, with executive authority in greater numbers than in any other public sector service industry. And for the majority of these women the route upwards was through nursing. A real, positive and determined effort must be made to counteract this side-effect of general management and to develop nurses for leadership positions in nursing and in the NHS generally (Clay 1986).

I realise that this view—to which I will return later—may not accord with some views expressed by feminist nurses and commentators. Indeed, I may well be criticised for insinuating that success for women is synonymous with success in male terms. Remember Professor Higgins's exasperated outburst: 'Oh why can't a woman be more like a man?'

Maleness and Femaleness

The opposite view, of course, is that rather than imbuing a female profession with male values, we should be working to assert, develop and generate confidence in nursing's 'femaleness'. Oakley (1984) explores this theme in her fascinating analysis of nurses, women, power and professionalism. She ends by asking what is so wonderful about being a professional, and challenging nurses to explore the Illich (1977) argument that professionalism in health care may actually be damaging to health—in terms of its disabling effect.

En route to this radical conclusion, Dr Oakley looks at the gender division in medicine and nursing, observing that in both professions men monopolise the top positions. Nurses need assertiveness training, she observes: 'If Florence Nightingale had trained her lady pupils in assertiveness rather than obedience, perhaps nurses would be in a different place now.' Miss Nightingale herself needed no assertiveness training; nor did she appear to have a problem with the interconnection of nursing and womanhood. Only later when such phrases as 'To be a good nurse one must be a good woman' could no longer be taken at face-value and began to smack of pious virtue and subservience, did we begin rather self-consciously, to pursue professionalism. Etzioni (1976) included nurses in his categorisation of the 'semi-professions' along with teachers and social workers. The female-ness of these occupational groups apparently gave them a flying start in the pursuit of semi-professionalism. 'If a profession is by definition male-dominated, then nurses might as well give up,' comments Dr Oakley. I do not, of course, agree. The professions are changing, and coming down from their pedestals. If nursing can take these few small steps into the realm of professionalism, then society will be the beneficiary and the image of the pro-fessions will be enhanced by the arrival of this key group of people.

The received wisdom at the moment is that nursing is a pro-fession complementary to medicine; intrinsically different, but of equal value. Whether or not this is true is not especially import-ant. What is important is that nursing is developing, perhaps for the first time since Miss Nightingale, a sense of its own goals and priorities which may not be the same as medicine's. This separate-ness, described by Alison Kitson (RCN 1986) as the distinction between 'getting better' (medicine) and 'feeling better' (nursing), has its roots in maleness and femaleness. Our newly rediscovered pride in the skills needed to help the patient feel better is surely linked with the recognition that the scientific, unemotional, logi-cal male world of medicine is only part of the story.

Of equal importance is the hard realisation that the world at large has no such fancy notions of equality between doctors and nurses. Doctors are educated, nurses are trained (sometimes); doctors have and use their knowledge, nurses do what comes naturally, doctors rely on research, nurses on kindness and common sense, doctors give the orders, nurses carry them out. And central to these powerful images is the fact that doctors are predominantly male, nurses predominantly female. The public may broadly like nurses and dislike doctors, but they have no doubt about which is the more powerful, knowledgeable and im-portant.

Let me give two examples of this kind of thinking. First, well-meaning observers often say that it would be good if professional training and education was opened up so that intelligent nurses could more easily train to be doctors. No-one ever mentions that students who opted for medicine, or who were coerced into it by parents and teachers, and who find themselves square pegs in round holes, might want to retrain as nurses. Nor does any one ever remember that many graduate nurses not only stay in nursing longer than conventionally trained students, but belie expectations by remaining at the bedside (Commission on Nursing Education 1985).

The second example concerns the supposed pull not of medicine, but of general management. In January 1986, the RCN launched a major press and public relations campaign to attempt to salvage something for nursing out of the implementation of the Griffiths report at every level in the NHS. We appealed for public support in fighting for a nursing head in each unit, working alongside the general manager and playing a real part in policy making. With the help of our advertising agency our message was distilled down to an unambiguous core, but still many people—most notably the politicians—chose to interpret our campaign as motivated by 'sour grapes'. Nurses had failed to pick up many of the new jobs and were fighting a rearguard action to preserve the status quo. It is indeed a pity that so few nurses have been appointed to general manager posts, but a far greater tragedy, which we have only partly averted, is the loss of so much nursing talent from nursing leadership positions. I fundamentally believe that nursing must be led by nurses and we can no longer say that is happening in the UK.

Mirrors and Images

The Griffiths experience has been a real blow to nursing's self confidence. It reminded us of where the power lies and of the stereotyped view of nurses and nursing that is still prevalent, even among fellow health service staff. Nursing shares its stereotypes with those of women in our society generally—the harridan, the angel, the nymphomaniac. It was fascinating that our Griffiths dilemma could best be turned into the slogan: 'Bring back the matron', which we could not for obvious reasons use, but which clearly evoked for many the battleaxe figure of the late lamented Hattie Jacques. She was a formidable figure, feared by one and all, but very firmly in control of the hospital—including the doctors–and always acting in the patients' interests. In the tabloids, the nurse who goes to work in the famine-stricken areas of Africa is always an 'angel', and anything connected with uniforms, nurses' homes and night shifts stimulates all kinds of fantasies about sexy nurses.

All this is now familiar territory thanks to the work of Salvage (1983) in this country and Kalisch and Kalisch (1982) in the USA. American nurses have been much quicker to realise the damage that is done to nursing by the continued primacy of these images and to challenge them wherever they are trotted out. Kalisch and Kalisch put it in a nutshell when they wrote:

'A consistently misrepresented image of the professional nurse ... can affect negatively the way in which the public thinks about nurses. In the 1980s, both consumers of health care services and health policy makers will be asked increasingly to consider the proper role and value of the nurse to the nation's health care industry. Statistics, documentation and rational argument concerning the nursing profession can make but little headway against constantly reinforced negative stereotypes of nurses ...'.

The work of Kalisch and Kalisch, quite apart from the intrinsic fascination of studying the portrayal of nurses in television, novels, films and so on, is important in underlining the gap between image and reality. It matters not a jot that nurses are becoming better able to argue their case, to feel comfortable with using research, to extend and develop their role, if the media continue to distort and misrepresent their work. If a nurse, or a particular nursing activity, fails to fit into one of the media images, it is either ignored or manipulated until it does fit.

Take the media 'problem', for example, when I took over as general secretary in 1982, at the height of a pay dispute. The *Daily Express* (17 September) ran a headline, 'Man on the side of the angels'. And the *Daily Mail* (9 July) photographed me surrounded by young women with the line: 'Man at the top in woman's world takes over as leader of 200,000 nurses.' The story ran: 'A nurse at 18, a sister at 25 and a matron at 33 sounds like the ideal career profile for the new leader of the Royal College of Nursing. Except his name is Trevor.' Even John Lloyd in the *Financial Times* (25 September) had trouble fitting a male

general secretary into the stereotypes: 'Clay may prove something of an iconoclast in the RCN, but only according to its own
lights. He has appeared much more like a (very moderate) union
leader than his predecessor, Dame Catherine Hall.'

Concern for the image of nurses and nursing and a desire for a
more positive portrayal is not—wholly—a symptom of professional vanity. It could well be that nurses are particularly
sensitive—doctors, lawyers and journalists all appear quite
unperturbed by the dreadful press they sometimes receive. But
nursing's problem is that the public like nurses the way they
are—or rather the way they imagine them to be: a heady mix of
the angel and the whore. To promote nurses as educated men
and women, standing up for their rights and the rights of the
patient, working in health centres, factories and schools as well
as in hospital, needing to pay the mortgage and the gas bill, and
subject to ordinary human foibles, stresses and strains is a difficult undertaking. But it is necessary and urgent to shatter the
illusions and promote the reality.

Let us return again to the notion of power. A study of the way
the words 'nurse' and 'feminine' were perceived in 30 language/
culture communities (Austin, Champion and Tzeng 1985)
showed that the image of the nurse was generally similar to the
feminine image—'good' and 'active' but also 'weak'. The authors
speculate whether the close correlation between 'nurse' and
'feminine' is because most nurses are women or because the
practice of nursing is linked to the act of mothering. 'As more
women enter traditionally masculine professions such as medicine and business will this result in a more powerful feminine
image?', they ask. Finally they pose the question which underlies
this whole chapter: 'Can nursing retain the positive aspects of
being linked with femininity and also become more powerful?'

Compulsory reading for any nurse struggling with these ideas;
enraged by the way she or he is seen by society, frustrated by her
or his apparent absence of power, excited by the satisfaction and
potential of nursing yet uncertain of the way forward, is a suc-
cinct piece by Fagin and Diers (1983) on nursing as a metaphor.
It begins with the familiar social situation: as your occupational
identity is revealed, the stereotyped images unfurl. Behind the
stereotype are a range of metaphors which influence language,
thought and action: nursing as a metaphor for mothering, for
class struggle, for equality, for conscience, for intimacy ('Nurses

do publicly what healthy people do for themselves behind closed doors'), and for sex. Fagin and Diers argue that 'something like the sum of these images makes up the psychological milieu in which nurses live and work'. They argue that most of these metaphors can be turned around and used positively, helping the nurse to become 'wistfully amused' by the reactions provoked rather than defensive and, one could add, depressed.

Women at Work

In the final section of this chapter I want to return to how the health service in general, and the nursing profession in particular, can make better use of this massively underutilised resource. There is, as we have shown, a workforce consisting of 90 per cent women, dominated in its managers, educators and its 'politicians' by men. The ideas of the women's movement have hardly been allowed overtly to influence nursing in Britain, but the obvious links between women's position in society and the nurse's position in health-care hierarchies are being made. To enable nurses to have a less circumscribed role in health care and to challenge the medical supremacy, their self-confidence must be built up so that they feel more comfortable with the techniques of politics and the use of power.

I very much like the words of Jo Ann Ashley, quoted in Chine and Wheeler (1985):

'For many years we have heard that nursing is at the crossroads. Nursing never seems to get over being at a crossroads. Indeed, nursing has been at a crossroads many times, but instead of taking a new road, leaders in the profession always choose to continue bearing the burden of continuing to live out the subservient role under the patriarchal system, rather than taking a new road that can lead beyond patriarchy. Nursing is no longer at a crossroads. It is at a turning point.'

The turning point here in Britain is that at a time when the need for nurses has never been higher, the supply is drying up. Not only is nursing failing to attract a sufficient number of recruits, it has also not found a satisfactory way of stemming the drop-out rate during training and is still nothing short of extravagant in the manner in which it allows qualified nurses to leave the profession, making no effort to encourage them to return.

A study commissioned by the RCN from the Institute of Manpower Studies (1986) showed that 40 per cent of qualified nurses had seriously considered leaving the NHS during the previous year. Of those who were thinking of leaving or who had already left, the vast majority said they would be attracted back not just by improved pay levels, but if the NHS were to provide creche and childcare facilities. Giving these provisions equal weight with improved pay shows how far the NHS has overlooked, and continues to overlook, the needs of the female workers who constitute 75 per cent of the 1,000,000 NHS workforce. The fact that women have put up with this for so long underlines the significance of their relative powerlessness and the dominance of the 'patriarchy'.

How far has the equal opportunities legislation influenced the health service? The Sex Discrimination Act 1975, which established the Equal Opportunities Commission, had a curious impact on nursing, quite unrelated to making the NHS an easier, more hospitable place for women—or men—with family responsibilities. It focused on two areas—making provision for men to train as midwives, which caused a major upheaval and ultimately facilitated only a handful of men with those particular career aspirations; and ensuring that job advertisements were scrupulously gender-free. It was, for example, no longer possible to advertise for a ward sister, except in certain circumstances where the job had to be filled by a woman. All jobs had to be open to men and women alike. It could well form a case-study about how the EOC marginalised what should have been its central concerns.

The feminist view would be that decision making in the NHS is largely carried out by those who do not have domestic commitments (the unmarried) or by those whose domestic commitments are undertaken by others (men). In those circumstances it is hardly surprising that the needs of working mothers have rarely been considered. At least as potent a reason, however, is that the NHS, like the First World War generals, has come to rely on a steady stream of eager, cheap, obedient recruits who form the backbone of the workforce and are replaced in due course by another cohort. Add to this the rigidity of the hospital as a 'total institution' in which bizarre routines are enforced upon captive sick human beings, such as being woken at 5.30 am, being kept obsessively clean and half-starved or fed with awful food.

Successive attempts to reform the in-patient's day (Ministry of Health, 1961) have come to nothing. It still remains ludicrously important to get the 'work' done by 10 am so that the consultants can visit a tidy ward. In the general hospital set-up this may to a small degree be understandable; in other settings—geriatrics, paediatrics, the mentally ill and handicapped—it is an anachronistic notion that should be scrapped.

There are many settings in which the bulk of nursing 'work' could be done between 9.30 am and 3 pm, allowing both women and men to meet their children from school and more easily combine paid employment with parenting. Instead, therefore, of expecting nurses with domestic commitments somehow to fit in with the system, it is surely time that the system itself underwent an overhaul.

Of course this is not the complete answer. Nursing will always remain a 24-hour service, but rigid staff systems often operate with no real justification other than tradition. We must move away from the kind of thinking which implies that if you cannot fit in with the system there is something wrong with you. We need to put meaning and action behind the cliche that nurses are the health service's most under-utilised resource.

And if anyone thinks this is an original idea, born out of the current manpower crisis and the growing assertiveness of women, let them consider a host of reports over the past three decades. Without exception they show how dependent the NHS is on married women and how important it is to accommodate them with their domestic commitments. *Marriage and Nursing* (1967) surveyed registered and enrolled nurses and came up with 15 specific proposals to make nursing more attractive to women with children. Many of the points are made in our own action plan at the end of this chapter. *Reserves of Nurses* (1975) confirmed the same message: flexibility of hours and better child care facilities were more important than improved pay for women wanting to return. Lisbeth Hockey's classic work *Women in Nursing* (1976) rigorously researched the subject and drew similar conclusions.

So how, therefore, do we create a better world for nurses in the NHS? I believe there is a role for management to be evangelical, to preach a greater ambition for women and to question the assumptions about social patterns that we have inherited. In that evangelical role, I include those in a position like myself and organisations such as trade unions and professional bodies to promote a new deal for women that they should not accept the opportunities or lack of them which are currently available if they choose nursing in the NHS.

The largest waste of resources in the NHS is the loss of qualified nursing staff. Three years of training and several years' experience are lost because managements have passively accepted existing attitudes to women and their pattern of work. Since everything else in the NHS is under new management, perhaps we can hope for an examination of these values which have tolerated such waste and which require a fifth of all nursing staff to be nurses in training, in order to keep up with the numbers being lost further up the line.

Nor is it just general social attitudes that are at fault. Nursing, as we have shown, has its own brand of discrimination against women. It is still based on a mixture of religious and military models, and is extremely hierarchical. It is not really surprising that when men began to enter general nursing in large numbers they progressed quickly up the promotion ladder, because although the profession is numerically dominated by women, the road to advancement is through a model in which the man committed to full-time work is given a head start. And the women who thrive are single, and able to give uninterrupted service. Rosemary Hutt (1985), in her study on chief officer career profiles, confirms that not only are chief officers in nursing unrepresentative as a whole, comprising a higher proportion of single women, but few have children, few have experience of work outside nursing and most said they had had no particular ambition.

Yet finding a speedy route to the conventional 'top' is not the whole story. I find myself agreeing with the view that nursing's higher echelons are at the bedside. But look at how we downgrade it: we train nurses to escape from bedside nursing, having put them through such intolerable strains during their training. And we only reluctantly offer post-basic opportunities to women who look as if they might drop out for family or other reasons. This lack of opportunity in training and work experience often lies at the root of later problems when the question of promotion arises.

Nursing and the NHS, strangely, do not have a healthy attitude to pregnancy. Whatever the statutory requirements, it is extremely difficult to carry out the full range of nursing duties as pregnancy advances, yet a large workforce ought to have within it the flexibility to deploy staff in other work. Effort put into enabling a woman to stay in work for as long as possible would clearly signal that she was wanted. And of course the national nursing uniform, among its many other failings, is incapable of accommodating pregnancy.

Once a nurse has a child the NHS is particularly negligent. If she decides to return early, the facilities in most hospital complexes for creches or nurseries are almost non-existent. Where they do exist, many operate office hours, which is hardly helpful to staff who have to work shifts. When the provision of nursery and creche facilities fell victim to the first round of cuts in NHS expenditure in 1976, it represented one of the most shortsighted savings there can possibly have been. Many hospital sites have huge numbers of women in all kinds of jobs working within a relatively small area for a single employer. Some attempts have to be made by NHS managers to evaluate the benefits of retaining trained staff, in budgetary terms alone, never mind the advantages of having experienced staff.

For some women the solution once their children are past the baby stage is to return to part-time work, using the fact that nursing is a 24-hour, seven days a week service to make arrangements which fit in with their husband's or other relative's availability. Over-zealous managers, meddling with shift patterns to make savings from the paybill, often do not realise that a half-hour change can wreck carefully planned domestic arrangements and maybe also force women out of nursing. Some authorities have experimented with ten or 12-hour shifts, which may make sense on paper but which create a nightmare of fatigue and stress for many nurses. The latest fad, internal rotation, is even more iniquitous, compelling nurses into a shift switchback which only the unattached and childless find tolerable. This thoughtless style of management may have worked while nurses were plentiful, but now the shortages are beginning to show, far greater consideration must be given to the lives of nurses outside work.

What happens to women who take a longer break from nursing? For them it is not just a matter of the practical facilities to come back to work in the NHS while raising a family. There is also the question of confidence and competence. The problem and some down-to-earth solutions were described recently by Irene Heywood Jones (1985). Although they are licenced to practice as nurses, they are acutely conscious that their skills date very quickly. It is this confidence gap which the NHS has so often failed to bridge, to its own considerable cost. What is required are back-to-nursing courses which update skills, give the nurse back her confidence and open the door to the NHS again. Such courses are run in a few places and by comparison with the investment required to start a new student nurse from scratch, they make economic sense for all concerned. In Portsmouth, for example, a highly successful back-to-nursing course is run in which participants pay a fee. There is always a surfeit of applicants.

The NHS has far to go. If the male-dominated world of banking can get it right, then so can the health service. The National Westminster Bank since 1981 has had a re-entry scheme offering women—or men—with career potential, the opportunity of a break of up to five years to raise a family. People on the scheme keep in touch by working at least two weeks a year, attending an annual seminar, and receiving monthly packs on developments in banking. If they return to work, they can come in at the same level and with a positive, career-minded attitude to take them upwards. There is much the NHS could learn from such schemes, not just to fulfil its social responsibilities, but also to benefit economically.

As the IMS survey showed, a staggering 40 per cent had thought seriously of leaving the NHS during the past year and 14 per cent had already left. The vast majority rated the provision of better childcare facilities as the main incentive which would draw them back into the NHS—along with improved pay. In a predominantly female profession it is scandalous that these issues have not before been seriously addressed by the service. This chapter began with an exploration of power. There could be no more appropriate starting place in the use of this newly honed weapon of power than in seeking implemention of a charter for women's employment.

The action plan for female nurses in the NHS consists therefore of the following points—(some of which, incidentally, could greatly enhance the lives of male nurses too):

1. Managers and health authorities must recognise that the service cannot continue to depend on young, unmarried women working full-time.
2. They must accept a different career model which recognises

the value of part-time work and experience gained outside employment.

3. Part-time working should be facilitated by formal job-sharing schemes and by altering where possible the routine of the patient's day to spread the work more evenly.
4. Nurses should be helped to cope with stress and with situations that lead to depression and demoralisation.
5. The economic arguments about proper facilities to help working women with children should be made forcefully.
6. A full network of creches, nurseries and after-school play facilities should be developed both on hospital sites and in the community generally.
7. Both men and women should be able to take leave both for childcare and to care for sick adult dependents.
8. Back-to-nursing courses should be provided in a way that is helpful to working mothers.
9. 'Stay in touch' schemes should be introduced to help women who leave to have children to keep up with developments in nursing.
10. A clinical career structure should be introduced with all kinds of imaginative links and ladders to help those who do not have conventional career patterns.

References

Austin, J. A., Champion, V. L. and Tzeng, O. C. S. (1985) Crosscultural comparison on nursing image. *International Journal of Nursing Studies*, 22 March: 231–39.

Chine, P. L. and Wheeler, C. E. (1985) Feminism and Nursing. *Nursing Outlook* 33 (2):74–7.

Clay, T. (1986) Where have all the women gone? *Lampada* 7, Spring. RCN.

Etzioni, A. (ed.) (1969) *The Semi-professions and their organisation: Teachers, nurses and social workers*. New York: The Free Press.

Equal Opportunities Commission (1977) *Equal Opportunities, a guide for employees*. Manchester: EOC.

Fagin, C. and Diers, D. (1983) Nursing as Metaphor. *New England Journal of Medicine*, July 14: 116–17.

Heywood-Jones, I. (1985) *Back to Nursing with Confidence*. London: William Heinemann Medical Books.

Hockey, L. (1976) *Women in Nursing*. London: Hodder & Stoughton.

Hutt, R. (1985) *Chief Officer Career Profiles : a study of the backgrounds, training and career experiences of regional and district nursing officers*. Brighton: Institute of Manpower Studies.

Illich, I. (1977) Disabling professions. In *Disabling Professions* (I. Illich *et al.* ed.). London: Marion Boyars.

Judge Commission on Nursing Education (1985) *The Education of Nurses: A New Dispensation*. London: RCN.

Kalisch, P. A. and Kalisch, B. J. (1982) Nursing on prime time television. *American Journal of Nursing*, **82** (2):264–70.

Ministry of Health (1961) *Pattern of the In-patient's day*. London: HMSO.

Nuttall, P. D. (1983) Male takeover or female giveaway? *Nursing Times*, January 12: 10–11.

Oakley, A. (1984) The Importance of Being a Nurse. *Nursing Times*, December 12.

Ramsden, G. A. and Skeet, M. H. (1967) *Marriage and Nursing, a Survey of State Registered and State Enrolled Nurses*. London: Dan Mason Nursing Research Committee.

Royal College of Nursing (1986) *Getting better, feeling better*. Griffiths campaign booklet based on Alison Kitson's work. London: RCN.

Sadler, J. and Whitworth, T. (1975) *Reserves of Nurses*. Office of Population Censuses and Surveys. London: HMSO.

Salvage, J. (1983) Distorted Images. *Nursing Times*, January 5: 11–15.

Waite, R. K. and Hutt, R. (1986) *Jobs and mobility of qualified nurses: A Report for the RCN*. Brighton: Institute of Manpower Studies.

CHAPTER 10

Professional trade unionism

When the RCN adopted the slogan 'The Professional Trade Union for Nurses' it provoked powerful feelings and reactions. For many, a trade union and a professional group are mutually exclusive. On one hand, the trade union approach is perceived to be primarily about self-interest and immediate matters such as wages and conditions; on the other, the professional approach is concerned with standards of nursing, the future development of the profession, and putting greater good above the immediate needs of members.

It is not my intention here to give a treatise on what is a profession and what is not. In the postwar years, many groups in society, especially white-collar workers, adopted the term 'professional' to signify that they should not be associated with the common practices of trade unions. They avoided the use of the word 'union' and preferred association: the Association of University Teachers, the Association of Scientific Technical and Managerial Staffs, etc. With some justification, many trade unionists saw this as spineless sophistry and feel that the RCN is tarred by the same brush.

In nursing, many have tried to perpetuate the divide between professional and trade union activities. It is a false divide. The real challenge is to find the balance between the effort that we put into both sides of the work of the RCN. In practice, we are seen by the public, who are the final arbiters, to be both a trade union which legitimately represents its members' direct interests and a professional organisation which promotes excellence in nursing and is prepared to be self-critical.

The issue centres on whether a nurse is prepared to leave her patients when she withdraws her labour during an industrial dispute. If you go on strike, you are a trade unionist and nothing else. If you refuse to leave the patient's side then you are a 'true' professional. I believe this is a false split and if the nurses in the UK ever found themselves in a position where their only choice was whether or not to go on strike then I would take the view that organisationally we had failed. A professional trade union seeks to ensure that its members are never put into that position. It is our task to find alternative techniques.

The debate about what are the professional aspects of nursing and what are the trade union aspects is particularly divisive and sterile. Virtually all the members who support the trade union activities of the RCN also see themselves as professional people, deeply concerned with the future of the profession and with the development of excellence in nursing. Many managers and nurse educationalists, however, have reinforced the distinction between professional and other activities when it suited their purposes. The distinction backfired on them when the new general managers appointed after the Griffiths Enquiry (1983) argued that professional advice was separate from actually managing the service. Many nurse managers found themselves placed in advisory roles with no control over the deployment of nurses. Those who have drawn distinctions between the professional and the trade union sides of nursing found general managers arguing there was also a distinction between the professional and the practical job of managing the service.

Every aspect of the organisation of nursing is of concern to us as professionals and trade unionists. We weaken our position if we lose either perspective, and weaken our credibility if we allow one approach to dominate. If we allow self-interest to dominate over what we know to be the long-term good of the service to the public then what we gain in the short term, we will lose ultimately.

Almost to the point of tedium the public and press focus on the RCN policy of not resorting to strike action. During each period of major industrial action in the health service, in 1979 and 1982, nurses have flocked to membership of the RCN. I believe that our policy is right for nurses in the NHS in the UK.

It is the right tactical stand because it represents an important pact with the public. I do not think it should be seen as the sole test of a professional stance; that must constitute much more, but it is a key element.

The RCN became a trade union in 1977 after considerable debate among the membership. Eventually, the step was taken to fall in line with industrial relations legislation which conferred important rights on trade unions. The RCN was already carrying out a wide range of industrial relations services for its members. It had established a stewards' network. It provided nurses with legal representation where they faced disciplinary action or were making claims for accident or injury. Under the legislation, passed by the Labour government elected in 1974, particular rights were now available to organisations which became certificated as independent trade unions. Employers were obliged to recognise their stewards and health and safety representatives. These were opportunities and rights which the RCN needed. The British Medical Association faced the same dilemma and reached the same conclusion.

The 'new unionism' has been widely scrutinised as the trade unions and the TUC have come to terms with the new reality under the Conservative government elected in 1979. To understand the stance taken by the RCN, the position of nurses and their employment must be viewed in its widest context. Our stance precedes the debate on 'new unionism' and goes further on many issues.

The difficulties that many unions have encountered are not solely the result of the Conservative government. The Conservatives have ridden a tide of feeling which was strong before 1979 and which would have taken a Labour government along with it, had it been re-elected. The signs were already there, with the firemen's strike and the Winter of Discontent. The Labour government of Jim Callaghan felt it had to show resolve in the face of the industrial tactics being used in the public sector or lose the confidence of the public.

I have always been amazed at the way in which public sector unions, and particularly the white collar ones, such as teachers and civil servants, have adopted an industrial model for action. The state is a very different employer from any other. Work in public service is not about making profit. It is about giving service. Ironically, the withdrawal of labour deprives the services whether it be teaching, road cleaning, refuse collection, or social security, but it does not necessarily put pressure on the government. For every vote of sympathy that such action can attract, a vote of anger will be delivered. The main balance sheet which a democratic government has to watch is the one affecting public opinion. There have been times when industrial action has publicised a case, drawing attention to it in a way which put the government on the spot. Many would take this view of the 1972 and 1974 miners' strikes. The miners commanded widespread public sympathy despite the disruption they caused. On the balance sheet of public opinion, the government were losing out seriously. It was the electorate which brought the Heath government down in 1974. Had Heath been re-elected he would have had a mandate for the government to stand up to the miners and we would have witnessed a different scene in the late 1970s. Margaret Thatcher had a clear mandate and took steps to ensure that the integrity of her government was maintained.

The miners are not a good example, because they had real economic power which by 1984 was much reduced. Most workers in the public sector have little real economic power of any kind. They have virtually nothing but the balance sheet of public opinion.

In the 1970s, the government tended to be inept and taken by surprise by industrial action in the public sector. Industrial action did then have the hoped-for effect of publicising a case, but this was only a passing phase. Most trade unionists would now recognise privately that government departments are prepared both practically and in public relations for almost any strike in the public sector.

The campaigns in the public sector are increasingly campaigns for public support, for pressure through public opinion to be brought on the government as employers. Given that recognition, I am surprised that so many public sector unions have failed to commit really large sums of money to the business of public relations, advertising, and the well-established techniques of persuasion.

Many nurses watched with concern the teachers' dispute which began in 1984, dragged on through 1985, and still appeared unresolved in the autumn of 1986. Only towards the end of that dispute did the real message about the state of the education service—of which teachers' pay was only one part— begin to get through. The message was one of concern about the state of the education system, its morale and the quality of teaching. The dispute left a residue of bitterness and broken working relationships which many must deeply regret and wish that some other method of campaigning had been found. The real campaign was persuasion. A large part of the persuasive effort seemed directed inwards towards members to convince them that the effort would pay off. Industrial action had become protest but there are other ways to do it.

Two myths about industrial relations and nurses need to be shattered. The first is that nurses are not powerful as a group in society and the second is that the public always loves the nurses.

Harold MacMillan is said to have advised his cabinet that there were three groups in the country that they should never fall out with: the Pope, the miners and the nurses. Because the nurses in the UK have not resorted to the use of mass strike action, both the public and politicians seem to have become complacent about the awesome power and the serious consequences a withdrawal of labour by nurses would have. It is nurses who keep people alive and safe in hospital 24 hours a day, seven days a week. In other countries, particularly those which do not have a socialised system of health care, nurses do strike. Few of the disputes last for more than two weeks, even where emergency services are being maintained and a number of nurses are refusing to join the strike, as happened in Ireland in 1980.

There are few examples of industrial action where all the nurses have gone on strike. Usually it is only a part of the workforce as it was in Ireland in 1980. Often nurses strike only because they know that other nurses would still go in. Alternatively, the strike is confined to one hospital and other hospitals take the strain. But where an all-out strike does take place, as in Israel in 1986, the results are quickly catastrophic. In Israel, legislation was passed ordering the nurses back to work under threats if imprisonment. Such was the horror it threatened that the government felt it could not ride out the crisis, and allow matters to be settled through the democratic negotiating process. The exercise of 'industrial power' in the form of an all-out strike very quickly moves from the arena of industrial relations into that of public policy. No government can stand by while issues of life and death rather than pounds and pence are at stake.

While RCN nurses are often accused of hypocrisy because they do not take industrial action, yet share its benefits, a fair amount of hypocrisy comes into play on the other side. I do not accept that the gains made by nurses in the UK have been through industrial action and I think the outcome of the 1982 dispute made that point clearly. It was the RCN's ballots, not industrial action which moved the dispute forward and improved the government's offer. Many of the staff, nursing or otherwise, only take industrial action because they know the worst that will happen is administrative inconvenience, and RCN nurses will ensure the service to patients is maintained. Even with that proviso, trade union officials from organisations which do support the use of industrial action privately admit that very few of their qualified nurse members actually left the bedside in 1982. The 24-hour shift system means that people in uniforms can be seen on demonstrations without actually being on strike.

The second great myth is that nurses are automatically popular. A short trip to the USA would disabuse the readers of that myth. The popularity and public pulling power that nurses have in the UK is the product of a conscious, long-term investment in public confidence. In the end the confidence and support which nurses can rely on when they ask for it is dependent on their pact with the public in the UK. This deep-seated trust did not drop out of the sky. It has been built up over the years by nursing leaders who recognised that there are no short, sharp routes to change. It is more important to take the long view, a long-term investment which has paid off, despite all the problems which nursing faces today.

Nurses face some of the most extreme dilemmas of any public sector workers. They serve the public at its most vulnerable and dependent. Action by them would have the most dramatic consequences almost immediately. Nurses work very closely with the public in a way that electricity power workers, for example, do not. Nursing is about an individual commitment to help and care for another person; an extremely difficult commitment to break. Nurses more than any other group have had to look at the consequences of their actions and consider the methods they should adopt to achieve their objectives. The model they have adopted in the largest numbers is that put forward by the RCN in its style of operation, organisation and tactics.

In the past ten years, members of the RCN have voted twice on the question of affiliation to the TUC and have overwhelmingly rejected it on both occasions. There are lessons to be learnt for the trade union movement in those resounding rejections. If they are learned well, I believe they will strengthen the whole union movement in the UK.

I do not wish to characterise organisations affiliated to the TUC as uncaring or incompetent in their choice of tactics. Much of the debate about new unionism which was initiated by Len Murray, General Secretary of the TUC, after the 1979 General Election was about addressing just these issues of style, representation, and tactics for settling disputes or pursuing objectives. The tactics of many of the new unions coming to the fore in the public sector were not regarded as appropriate or effective by the public. The size of nursing confronted it with all the difficulties and economic problems faced by other public sector unions. Yet we have chosen different courses of action.

There is a secondary debate about whether we should be involved in 'politics'. It is incredible that so many people in nursing have deluded themselves that they are not part of the political process. It was true that for as long as consensus existed among the political parties about the future of the NHS nursing had very little need of the political campaigning to which we have recently resorted over the Griffiths Report.

From 1948 until the mid-1970s, the prosperity enjoyed by the NHS and the political consensus to support it meant that in most disputes nursing could expect to be heard in the corridors of power as a matter of right. Nursing during this period often failed to get the changes it wanted. This had more to do with divisions within nursing than with a failure to engage in external political debate and public campaigning.

Nursing has always been high on the political agenda. We may not be in one party's camp but no politician can afford to ignore a service which consumes £3 out of every £100 that the government have to spend. We represent well over 600,000 people on the professional register of the UKCC, the majority of whom are employed in the National Health Service. The NHS is the largest single employer in the country. Nursing and health are of concern to every citizen and affect every constituency in the land. Directly or indirectly the political parties have always had to take an interest. Political activity for nurses is a legitimate alternative to walking out on patients. Economic constraints mean that the cosy world in which nursing has lived has been changed forever. The rejection of affiliation to the TUC was a rejection of a style and model of activity. The lessons of that rejection are many.

Many of the women in nursing are young, many work part-time. I am continually asked why the RCN does not affiliate to the TUC. My answer is that the real questions are not for the RCN but for the TUC and individual unions in the movement. I think the other unions have to ask themselves, as John Edmonds, who sat on the Nurses and Midwives Whitley Council for the GMBATU, suggested at the 1986 TUC Congress, why it is that so many of the new generation of people involved in work, both women and part-timers, find the traditional image of trade unionism so unpalatable. The nurses' rejection of the TUC in 1979 was a warning of a wider problem that the industrial model applied to the public sector was running into. I think we have come up with a formula in nursing which will have wider applications than just to the health service.

I believe public sector unions have various advantages which they have failed to use. They have large memberships and a simple structure for negotiating compared with the multitude of negotiations which have to be undertaken by traditional private sector unions. The large general unions enjoy status and power with massive resources at their disposal. The smaller and medium-sized public sector unions, such as teachers and nurses, enjoy a homogeneity which gives them a different strength. The problems in public service unions are spread across the whole country and not confined to particular localities like ship-building or coal-mining. Groups like nurses and teachers are generally well understood by the public, making the job of explanation easier. The public have an interest and involvement in the services which are provided.

Many public sector unions now clearly understand that the success or failure of a campaign may depend as much on the balance sheet of public opinion. Not all may wish to go as far as nursing in maintaining a self-denying ordinance on industrial action. We were once seen to be on the outside of trade union thinking on this issue. In October 1986, however, at the conference of the Institute of Personnel Management, Norman Willis, General Secretary of the TUC acknowledged that: 'Increasingly members will be looking to their unions to provide progress without strikes and without pickets'. It does not yet seem to me that many trade union executives have matched this recognition with a commitment of resources to alternative campaigning, especially in the media.

Nursing has looked at the possibility of limited industrial action. During the 1979 health service dispute, the RCN Council set up a committee under the chairmanship of June Clarke to look at 'professional action'. Professional action was to be separate from industrial action, and somehow more acceptable. It seems to me that professional action was born out of frustration and a sense of helplessness during a particularly bitter dispute; however, the idea was seriously flawed despite the hard work of the committee. If the RCN had gone down that road, the public would not have drawn the fine distinction; professional action would have been seen as industrial action. The distinction reflects the false division which has caused the College so much trouble and the sophistry into which nurses are commonly guilty of slipping. This debate reflects a tendency among nurses to go down the road of the major industrial unions, including the adoption of their rhetoric and tactics.

It is not enough simply to have self-denying ordinance against the use of industrial action. We need to have answers for members when they want to achieve change. We have to provide them with outlets which they feel are effective. I believe that we have to go wholeheartedly into alternative, political, ways of bringing pressure to bear on government. We cannot afford to be half-hearted. If the membership wish to avoid the use of industrial action they have to be willing to commit money and subscriptions to winning the argument. Advertising and high-profile communications do not come cheaply. In the RCN, we now give a higher proportion of our budget to communication than almost any other union or professional organisation. When we undertook the Griffiths advertising campaign in 1986 we spent £250,000 on full-page advertisments over several days.

We also have to try to avoid being reactive. The hardest argument to win is a defensive one. A professional trade union, in the sense of being an effective trade union in the public sector needs to anticipate events and policy debates and intervene on behalf of its members to try to win the argument from the outset. We now see increasing recognition of this in the appointment of parliamentary officers and public relations staff in many unions.

Second, the RCN is seen to be outside the trade union world because of its use of balloting. The RCN was balloting its members before the Conservative government introduced the 1984 legislation. Many people get confused about the RCN's system of balloting. Even where it is conducted as a proxy vote to an Emergency or Annual General Meeting, it is nevertheless a postal vote for all members. As a consequence of this, the RCN has always needed to keep a register of its members' addresses.

The ballot approach became not just a good internal system of keeping the College and its leadership in touch with members, but also a powerful weapon in the 1982 dispute. The same trade unionists who despaired of the outcome of the RCN vote on the TUC affiliation in 1979 cheered when the results of the RCN ballot on pay in 1982 delivered a resounding rejection to the offer of 6.4 per cent increases. That ballot had credibility with the public and altered the balance sheet of public opinion. The government had to move. The ballot as a regulator of our actions and a test of support is both an important internal mechanism which draws on the collective wisdom of the majority of the members, and a weapon which gives us the moral high ground in public debate. These are lessons which other trade unions only now seem to be learning. In the *Financial Times* (1985), labour correspondent David Brindle reviewed the progress the RCN was making and observed that during the lifetime of the Conservative government we had been the fastest-growing union in the UK, expanding from 101,000 in 1978 to 255,000 by the middle of 1986. He asked whether or not the RCN could be regarded as a 'proper union', 'Some would argue that the RCN remains a long way from being a proper union. Its non-affiliation to the TUC sets it apart from the mainstream labour movement.' A year later the problems of strikes and balloting no longer seemed to set the RCN outside the mainstream of trade union experience. Other unions have, through necessity, had to come to the formula we have established. They have arrived there through bitter experience, much of which I think could have been avoided if there had been a proper analysis of the true position.

While recognising the value of balloting, I would be the first to admit that we have a long way to go in developing political, public relations and campaigning techniques to provide our members with real, effective alternatives for getting change and progress in pay, conditions and in the health service. Clearly it is a matter of finding a better alternative.

Professional trade unionism faces the problem of managing the tensions between members' immediate demands and the broader view of the needs of nursing and the public. This is often a difficult but important tension. In 1986 we came under considerable pressure from the practice nurses in our own membership because we had highlighted serious gaps in the standards of some practice nurses to the Cumberlege Review of Community Nursing. The Council of the RCN in September 1986 adopted a resolution reminding members of their duty to patients with AIDS and that any refusal of care on grounds other than lack of training would open the individual nurse to charges of professional misconduct. Few other organisations would discuss problems with sections of their membership publicly or give such a forceful warning on such a sensitive issue.

It would be much more simple to adopt the model which takes whatever any group of members say, if they have a direct interest, and simply articulate it publicly. At times we have to question members' views and fears and challenge them where self interest is being pushed against the interest of the public and nursing.

In primary health care and in the reform of nurse education the RCN has spoken openly and frankly about the failings of the current systems of care. These activities are not simply a spin-off from the trade union work of the College. They consume as much of its time, often more. They command the resources to make them work both in the Department of Nursing Policy and Practice and in the Institute of Advanced Nursing Education. The RCN has always provided courses for nurses all over the world in nursing in its own right. The autumn of 1986 saw the establishment of courses in the treatment and care of AIDS patients. Our professional work is about making things happen, not just lobbying government or providing a platform for debate. We sponsor primary research such as the work of the Daphne Heald Research Unit, and that of Alison Kitson on standards of care. It is activities like these that are the real test of a professional trade union.

I do not claim that all that we put together in the recipe which we call professional trade unionism is perfect. But I do think it is a powerful combination which commands public support and is ahead of the generation of trade unions trying to develop a 'new unionism' from old organisational structures. The acid test of a policy is whether or not it has worked for our members' representation over pay or in pursuit of new health policies emanating from the collective wisdom of nursing.

The Struggle for a Just Reward

Nurses' pay is a problem for any government. Nursing is one of the largest sections of the public workforce. The nursing staff of the NHS (which includes auxiliaries and nursing assistants) amounts to half of all the NHS staff, almost 500,000 in total. The pay bill accounts for £3 out of every £100 that the government has to spend. The annual decision on nurses' pay is one of the main decisions government has to make in one of its most public departments.

The struggle for a just reward for nurses has been dogged over the years by lack of unity, by the crude public image of nurses and by the complicating effects of inflation which have eroded the few gains made. For most of the period since 1948, nursing representation was generally fragmented and many nurses were in no organisation at all. The workforce in 1966 was approximately half the size it was in 1983 and was only just entering a period of rapid expansion. The first cracks appeared in the Whitley structure in 1968 when the settlement of the nurses' pay award was referred to National Board for Prices and Incomes. The 1970s saw a series of campaigns run by the RCN in an attempt to put pressure on government as it increasingly set the parameters on pay. The economic optimism of the postwar years when the Whitley system was set up had gone for ever. Such a system was totally unable to cope with the rocketing inflation of the 1970s and the constraints which all governments attempted to put on public sector pay demands. The result was over a decade of instability, a series of campaigns by nursing organisations and a series of government enquiries into nurses' pay which resulted in little more than standing still on very low salaries. The only exception was the Halsbury Report of 1974.

Nursing is dogged by its public image. Because most nurses are women, successive governments and NHS management have devalued the quality of the service that is given, seeing it as little more than an extension of family caring. When the Clegg Commission came to look at nurses' pay, there was extreme anger in the profession that they could still be so insensitive as to compare nurses with secretaries and insurance clerks. Despite some good work in the Clegg Commission the idea is still abroad that many nurses' incomes are secondary in the household. The figures from the RCN's recent manpower study (IMS, 1986), show that 33.6

per cent of qualified members were single. In the total workforce the figure is even higher. Students, who make up 20 per cent of the workforce, include an even higher proportion who are single. There is also increasing evidence from our members in areas of the country such as the north-east, where the recession has hit hardest, that many married nurses bring the main income into the household. By adding those who are single to the number of male nurses and to the likely number who are now the main breadwinners it is clear that a majority of nurses provide the main domestic income of their households. Yet the myth continues that nurses' pay is secondary and supplementary.

The effects of inflation in the 1970s and early 1980s eroded the value of awards made to nurses. As each enquiry was held nurses hoped for justice, only to find that their award was a catching-up exercise quickly eroded by inflation. And these awards failed to address the structural problems which had developed in nursing pay.

1974 saw the establishment of the Halsbury Inquiry, with awards of 20–40 per cent. The inflation of 1975/1976 and the pay restraint of the latter half of that decade quickly undermined the gains. The Clegg award in 1980, which the Conservative government undertook to honour in the course of the election year, was seen by nurses as dealing with the problems of the late 1970s rather than preparing for the '80s. When the Conservative government does its pay calculations the Clegg awards are always taken as the start of the 1980s. Clegg itself was quickly eroded by the first of Geoffrey Howe's budgets, the extension of VAT and the consequent inflation in costs for people on low incomes. The second oil shock saw inflation once again rise to over 20 per cent, quickly undermining the gains which had been made and storing up further trouble in the NHS in 1982.

The years from 1970 to 1982 saw a series of public campaigns by the RCN. This reflected the recognition that the determination of pay for nurses had moved out of employer/employee bargaining and into the sphere of public bargaining. It was a series of very effective campaigns but the cycle became disappointingly repetitive. After a settlement or enquiry which often saw the nurses through an election, the problems returned. 1974 saw the first major campaign by the RCN—'Raise the Roof'—which sought to do just that and raise the level of pay generally. The campaign in 1979 for 'Pay not Peanuts' took up the theme of low pay among nurses, and in 1982 the theme of 'Bridge That Gap' reflected the fact that once more the gains which nurses had briefly made were being eroded in comparison to other groups, especially since the Conservative government was being selective in its treatment of workers in the public sector, with generous awards to the police and armed forces.

By the time we reached the dispute of 1982 we had behind us three cycles of awards, each of which had been quickly eroded by inflation. Nor were any of these awards able to tackle the pressing need for the structure of nurses' pay to be changed and a clinical career structure introduced. With this experience behind it the RCN went into the 1982 dispute. 1982 was also the year that I became General Secretary, taking up the reins on 11 July 1982 when the dispute was well under way.

For many RCN members and to much of the public the dispute appeared to be a question of short-term justice and how nurses would be treated in comparison with other groups during that year. From previous experience that seemed an inadequate perspective. In the early stages, the government were offering neither an adequate settlement nor the prospect of any system that would guarantee the future.

The first offer gave nurses an increase of 6.4 per cent, a differential increase compared to the 4.5 per cent being offered to other groups. It was roundly rejected. 61,954 nurses in RCN membership voted, with almost two to one against acceptance (41,297 against and 20,657 for). That vote was an important signal to the government that the nurses could not be bought off easily, but it was also a warning to many in the nursing profession. There is no doubt that there was a school of thought that would have been prepared to accept the first offer and believed that when it was put to the RCN membership they would settle the whole dispute by accepting and being happy with the differential. The prospects of the other unions continuing the campaign without the wholesale support of the RCN, easily the largest nurses' union, were very small.

The government then altered its offer but kept within the same framework. Essentially the settlement was to be about that single year and the offer was raised to 7.5 per cent. Strength of feeling in the NHS was running very high and public support for the nursing case following the ballot presented the government with a serious problem. The nurses had taken the moral high ground through balloting at a time when the government were lambasting other unions about their lack of balloting and unrepresentative activity. On 26 August the 7.5 per cent offer was put to the members in a ballot. The total voting increased by almost 30 per cent to 86,600, with 28,534 voting to accept the offer and a massive 58,143 voting to reject it.

As the argument continued throughout the summer it broadened from pay to a concern for the whole of the NHS. There can be no doubt that it was the wider arguments about the NHS surrounding the 1982 dispute that put the Conservative government on the spot about whether the NHS was 'safe in their hands' during the 1983 election. The campaign killed the ambitions of some politicians to introduce insurance schemes into the NHS.

After the second ballot the government realised that they were going to have to offer more than just a one-off settlement to the nursing profession. It was at this point that discussions about the establishment of a Pay Review Body for nurses began.

Eventually, the government offered a two-year pay package which did not represent a great improvement on the amount of money but offered an independent review body for the pay of nurses, midwives, health visitors, other nursing staffs and the professions allied to medicine.

That package was finally put to the membership of the RCN with a recommendation to accept in December 1982. The membership voted in larger numbers than ever (98,735) with the overwhelming majority in favour of the package (82,824 for, 15,911 against). That vote represented a vote of cautious trust in the leadership of the College and a gamble that the Review Body would be able to come up with something more sustained than the previous quick fixes which nursing had received.

The acceptance of a two-year deal clearly meant that nursing had to wait until after the 1983 election, with the risks this entailed of a different government not implementing the guarantees won in 1982. I think, however, that we had every reason to be confident we could hold any government to the agreement. There were other reasons for accepting the offer at that point. Between August, when the RCN had last voted and taken the moral high ground, the various forms of limited industrial action from the other unions were beginning to have an effect on the service. Many of the RCN's members were on the receiving end of these measures and were having to fill in the gaps to keep patients' services going. Those in the unions committed to industrial action were having to take it to its logical conclusion and this was not a road which even they wanted to follow.

Many members of the traditional trade unions directed their frustration and some of their venom at the RCN and its members. Limited action had a particularly divisive effect from which future tacticians would do well to learn lessons. Again in 1982 the question of RCN affiliation to the TUC was raised and rejected. In my view it had much to do with members' own experience of what happened when public service unions tried to bring an industrial model into operation in the public sector. The rejection of TUC affiliation also reflected a reaction to the control of the dispute by the TUC health services committee. It was seen to be directing events and instructing unions on courses of action. For many nurses this raised the spectre that the independence of the RCN and its no-strike rule would be in jeopardy. The reaction to this was very strong. The RCN saw a huge surge in membership during that time as nurses joined in their thousands.

The work of the Review Body so far has demonstrated that the decision we made in 1982 was the right one. Nurses showed considerable restraint as they waited for the first report. This report proved to be little more than a holding operation in 1984. The 1985 settlement saw increases of between 9 per cent and 14 per cent targeted at the qualified grades with the management grades receiving just 5 per cent increases. Despite the government staging of the award, which deprived nurses of actual cash, the base line for the following year's increase was effectively raised. When the 1986 award of 8 per cent was announced the investment had clearly paid off. Nurses had achieved a pay position ahead of their previous best after Halsbury in 1975. The government, however, again angered nurses by depriving them of three months increase in that year.

In 1985 the College anticipated that the government, asking everyone else to exercise restraint and with an unstated pay target of 3 per cent, would react badly to large increases for nurses, even those proposed by an independent pay review body. The government reaction was to stage the award in both 1985 and 1986. But by raising the issue and campaigning before the announcement the RCN focused enough public attention on the government to ensure that it did not actually reject some recommendations, as had happened to doctors for several years.

I believe it was right to take the long view in 1982 and to break out of the cycle of short-term settlements. The other unions now recognise that this judgement has paid off. In 1986 at its conference, COHSE's then Assistant General Secretary Hector Mac-Kenzie publicly defended the Review Body:

'Mr Hector Mackenzie, COHSE's Assistant General Secretary and Chairman of the Staff Side of the Nursing and Midwives Negotiating Council, told the Conference yesterday that the Review Body had become a thorn in the side of the government and an embarrassment to it.

His enthusiasm for the Review Body contrasts with the cautious if not hostile attitude of the TUC affiliated health workers' unions at the time the body was set up in 1982.' (*Financial Times*, June 1986)

The strength of our position lies in our long-term investment in public confidence. Industrial action is by its very nature an act of last resort, and invariably short-term. As a consequence, settlements are often short-term, addressing only immediate problems. I think the review body system, backed by sustained public and political pressure, is a better system than that of the 1970s.

For the future there are two points which I would make. The first, as I have shown in Chapter 2, is that we are about to see a change in the market forces affecting nursing. In the next decade the drop in the number of 18-year-old school leavers and the increased opportunities for those with basic qualifications to enter other professions will intensify what is already becoming a problem of sustaining recruitment to schools of nursing. We are treating more patients than ever before, and they are sicker and more dependent. The option of diluting the numbers of qualified nurses to solve the manpower problem will quickly produce public concern about standards and quality of service.

The second point is about the suggested absorption of the nursing pay review body into some omnibus public sector pay review. Such proposals are currently being considered in vague terms by the opposition parties. I warn that we will not lightly give up an independent review body for nurses' pay. The review body system which covers doctors, the armed forces, the police and top salaries may be seen by many a system of privilege. The Nurses'

Review Body is about justice for nurses and some return on the unique pact we have freely made with the public. All the signs are that the public expects the politicians to stick to that pact. Despite all of this, nurses are still appallingly low paid by any standard. Failure to correct this will damage the whole of the health service and the RCN will fight hard to see this does not happen.

Campaigning for Change

I believe that our public profile and campaigning on issues outside pay and conditions is important to the public. We have recently embarked on a programme highlighting issues of broader concern to the public. We are involved in striving for reform in nursing education. A radical change from the existing apprenticeship system towards a system based more closely on education is needed. We are pressing for a change in primary health care and an extended role for nursing, a move which must come if the government is to have any hope of fulfilling the objectives of extending primary health care to the vast majority of the population.

In 1986 the College was forced into a defensive campaign about the changes which were being made in the NHS management following the reforms advocated in the Griffiths Inquiry. As I have shown, we applied high-profile publicity and campaigning on an issue which affected relatively few people's jobs in an industrial relations sense but which was central to an organisation concerned about standards of nursing care and treatment.

September 1986 saw the publication of two documents illustrating the RCN's willingness to make wider alliances and to take a high profile. The first was joint research, *Public Expenditure on the NHS: Recent Trends and Future Problems*, sponsored with the Institute of Health Services Management and the British Medical Association. This has played a significant role in untangling the debate on NHS funding and helped the public and politicians to understand why the hospital service is having such a difficult time within overall budgets which appear to be expanding significantly. It also ensured that the NHS received an unexpectedly large boost in the 1986 Autumn statement by the Chancellor.

The second was the RCN's own *Manifesto on Nursing and Health* (1986), reprinted as an appendix to this book, which pulled together the main strands we wanted to highlight for the political parties on the future of nursing. The manifesto was directed at the public and politicians and set out our objectives and rationale in the bluntest possible terms. The campaign which followed gave a clear picture of the change in approach that the RCN has taken. It is throwing itself wholeheartedly into alternative techniques for influencing the public and achieving necessary change for nurses. For us it is a better road.

It is impossible to put down a recipe for what are really questions of strategy, tactics, style and approach for organisations in very different situations. But I think that the experience of nurses has made them tackle issues which some public sector unions are now only beginning to face. Let me summarise this.

Argument

1. The false division in debate between professional issues and industrial relations and management questions should be rejected.
2. All public sector unions need to debate the fundamental difference between the state as an employer and private companies.
3. The balance sheet of public opinion has become the arbiter in public sector disputes in the absence of formal machinery.
4. Effective trade unions must be able to address the content and objectives of their members' work, not just the terms and conditions.
5. Most public sector changes are preceded by some public or internal party debate. There are few surprises in the public sector.
6. A long-term approach is needed where the public sector is not subject to 'market fluctuations'.

Preparation

1. Public sector unions and professional organisations need to re-examine the balance of their budgets and break from the historical concentrations on traditional industrial relations activity.
2. More resources must be committed to parliamentary and re-

search activities to anticipate problems and develop solutions.
3.   A change in emphasis needs a change in attitude to union subscriptions and their level. Members get what they pay for. Many pay much less to protect their job than to insure their car.
4.   More resources should be committed to better information for members and to making the leap into issue-based public relations and advertising needed to move the public balance sheet of opinion.

Action

Much action in the public sector is protest, not economic muscle. Some ideas for action include:

1.   Clearer alliances with the interests of the consumers of the service.
2.   Resources for public relations and national advertising where necessary.
3.   Where 'strike funds' and 'political funds' have been tests of union commitment, the absence of 'persuasion funds' committed to winning the public argument has been a serious weakness.
4.   Public relations and political lobbying need to be developed beyond party affiliation.
5.   A shift in local priorities for unions and a greater commitment to involvement in public debate.
6.   Study how single issue groups such as voluntary organisations and the environment pressure groups use the techniques of protest and public relations.

References

Clegg Report (1980) *Standing Commission Pay Comparability, Report No. 3, Nurses and Midwives*. London: HMSO.
Department of Health and Social Security (1986) *Neighbourhood Nursing—a Focus for Care* (Cumberlege Report). London: HMSO.
Griffiths Inquiry (1983) *NHS Management Inquiry Report*. London: DHSS.

Griffiths Circular (1984) HC(84), 13 June 1984, *Health Services Management, Implementation of the NHS Management Inquiry Report*. London: DHSS.

Halsbury (1974) *Report of the Committee of Inquiry into Pay and Related Conditions of Nurses and Midwives*. London: HMSO.

Maynard, A. and Bosanquet, N. (1986) *Public Expenditure on the NHS: Recent Trends and Future Problems*. London: Institute of Health Services Management.

Review Body for Nursing Staff, Midwives, Health Visitors and Professions Allied to Medicine chaired by Sir John Hedley Greenborough. London: HMSO. 1st Report 1984; 2nd Report 1985; 3rd Report 1986.

Royal College of Nursing (1985) *AIDS: Nursing Guidelines*. London: RCN.

Royal College of Nursing (1986) *Manifesto for Nursing and Health*. London: RCN.

Waite, R. and Hutt, R. (1986) IMS Manpower Study *Jobs and Mobility of Qualified Nurses*. Institute of Manpower Studies, University of Sussex.

CHAPTER 11

Conclusion

Powerhouse for Change

In Greek drama, there is a device called *deus ex machina*: the god comes down out of the sky (on a pulley) at the end of the play to sort out a plot which has become hopelessly tangled. Nursing looks to a *deus ex machina* every time the going gets rough. It puts its faith in single solutions which come from nowhere. This leads to disappointment and frustration as the solutions turn out to be partial and the underlying problems remain. We must stop relying on single solutions and the kindness of others to solve our problems and recognise the multi-layered world in which we live.

A book which takes such a sweeping look at nursing can only deal superficially with some issues. Whole books have been written about matters which are given only one chapter here. There are issues within the chapters on ethics and education which could command a book to themselves. Many of these books have been written already and I hope that I have acknowledged them where I have borrowed or been inspired by their contents. But nursing has plenty in print on single issues and very little about bringing them together into an overview. The bookshelves of nursing libraries reflect the problems of nursing. All the issues are there, lined up and neatly compartmentalised. Mountains of material from the bedside and on clinical issues; the remainder tidily set out in politics, trade union affairs, professional organisation, professional issues, economics, women, ethics, education. The active world of government decision-making and public debate is not the tidy world of library shelves where there is a place for everything and everything is in its place.

In mapping out where I think nursing should go in the immediate future I hope you will not expect to find my suggestions tidy and satisfying. If they were it would reflect an unreal world.

Government policy and nursing policy debates reflect contradictions and dilemmas because they deal with change and uncertainty.

Nursing must choose the best road forward given all the pressures I have tried to highlight in this book. That road may not always satisfy those who look for perfection on particular issues but I hope also that the road forward should not represent the lowest common denominator in nursing or pure pragmatism in dealing with government.

There is a pessimism abroad in nursing at the moment about the possibilities of achieving change. Too many nurses are willing to give up the fight, whether for education, pay or an extended role for nursing, before it has even started. I do not share that pessimism. I take the view of Dr Mahler, Director-General of the World Health Organisation: 'If millions of nurses in a thousand different places articulate the same ideas and convictions about primary health care and come together as one force then they could act as a powerhouse for change' (*WHO Features*, WHO, July 1985). This view is based on more than just optimism that things will come all right. I believe there are steps and stances which we in nursing can take to improve dramatically the likelihood of getting what we want.

First I believe that more nurses and nursing leaders need to take an overview, need to be more aware of the outside forces which are at work in politics, in the economy and in the changing values of the public. Of these the outlook of the public is the most important: to it everything in a democratic society must eventually bend.

Within the changing values of the public are the many changes taking place in social and moral values. Some of them nursing must meet fully, as with the demand for dignity and choice in treatment or greater access to information. On these society is broadly agreed. Where society is divided, as on abortion, or in-vitro fertilisation, nursing must be careful not to take sides. Individual nurses who hold strong views must ensure that their possession of a precious skill does not lead them to deny patients the choice they demand and to which they have a right. Where the system denies those rights nurses must learn to speak out. The public must know whose side we are on.

The values of society give a greater emphasis than ever before to the rights of women. I do not think we can claim in nursing to have reflected that, either in our attitudes to women as patients or in our attitudes as managers of the largest female profession in the UK.

Nursing is one of the central images of women in our society. If Florence Nightingale had run those assertiveness classes, I wonder how our society and health care system might now be looking. We must not repeat that error either in our schools of nursing nor within our nursing organisations. I believe that it is the duty of the RCN, as it is of the health service, to find ways of liberating the women in nursing from both practical and social constraints on their participation in politics. The release of that potential is one of the necessary prerequisites for the success of nursing in the future. The power of nursing will be the power of hundreds of thousands of women when combined with clear policies.

Examining society's values must be matched by an examination of society's needs. I commend the approach of the UKCC Project 2000 group, who started work looking at future health needs and the changing pattern in society. The public are only marginally aware of the changes in population, in new conditions and treatments. We must keep them clearly in view and explain them repeatedly to the public and to our members. What we want for nursing must match what society will need in the future. A mismatch will be fatal for our profession.

Where society is faced with a growing number of elderly people and they demand dignity and care in their everyday domestic and personal needs nursing cannot afford to be seen to treat these needs as 'non-nursing duties', passing them to others. Where ethnic and cultural differences present challenges for the health service nursing must not dismiss these but learn to change. Too often in the past we have been too slow to respond.

This is the real pact with the public, meeting their needs, respecting their values. The other parts of that pact with the public are shorter-term commitments compared to this basic outlook.

Being in tune with public needs is not enough by itself to get change and progress. Other conditions must be met. An awareness of the political and economic issues of the day is necessary. For the forseeable future that means a recognition of the severe economic problems which the UK is experiencing and the effect this is having on public spending, including health. We need to recognise that even without those economic pressures the escalation in health care costs could not go on. Our current economic difficulties simply make the search for more effective ways of delivering care imperative. Nursing has much to offer in this area, a fact recognised by the WHO in its review of directions in health for the future. Nursing can combine the skills and the quality with affordability and we should not be coy about highlighting this. It is the message every government wants to hear.

We need also to be more aware of directions in health care. Despite the fact that 90 per cent of nurses continue to work in hospital and institutional settings we must take on board that the development of primary health care with an emphasis on prevention and health promotion has now reached the top of the political agenda. The provision of long-term care in the community has been there for over a decade. If our proposed reforms in education reflect what we have today the public will not forgive us for failing to meeting their needs tomorrow.

Without this overview of forces working on nursing and health, any organisation, professional or trade union, could deliver very little. Some of the strongest professions, such as the lawyers, or trade unions like the printers', have found in the last decade that if you set your face against changes in society eventually you will lose society's sympathy. Organisation and unity are, however, very important. Lack of them has been the downfall of nursing on many occasions in the past. Lack of unity has destroyed previous attempts at reform in nurse education. The RCN now represents every type of nurse. The major exception is the midwife. I believe that midwifery is a major branch of nursing, not a separate tree. I feel that in the recent past the midwives have enjoyed the shade and support of nursing but have sometimes repaid that with the pursuit of self-interest in education and pay. I believe that it is time for the RCN to follow that philosophy to its logical conclusion, to recruit and provide service and representation to midwives, 99 per cent of whom are nurses and have never seen themselves as anything else.

The wide service which the RCN provides for the many entities in nursing produces many internal conflicts. It is better by far that they are resolved within the RCN and within nursing than displayed on the public stage. Such displays of division have in the past only led to stalemate and to events moving forward without nursing having its full say. This is a plea not for lowest common denominator politics but for more discipline among those who may disagree with the outcome of a particular debate. In the long term the image of squabbling disunity serves only the opponents of nursing.

The growth in the size of the RCN has, I believe, been to the advantage of everyone in nursing. It has provided the resources to put nursing and its issues on the public stage by new methods. The advertising campaign on general management in January 1986 is merely a taste of what can be done by uniting on an issue and concentrating resources. The closer that nursing comes to being able to speak with one voice the better I believe it will be for all. I include in that the many entities and groups within nursing. What they may feel they lose in identity was often sectional vanity, what they gain in strength in their moments of need is immeasurable.

We must continue to tread the careful path of professional trade unionism and carry the support of the public. In forsaking the use of industrial action we must, and will, find new methods which build on our strengths. We have to reject the cynical view that public support has never brought any results in the past as false. The truth is that we have not really tried to organise and focus it on government. Blurred sympathy for the down-trodden nurse was never a basis for change. What we project in the future must be organised and clearly focused. I am confident that the public will repay that part of our pact with them and that successive governments will have to respond. Nothing is absolute about this. The pact is voluntarily given and we would not accept no-strike agreements being imposed. For the forseeable future I believe this is the best posture to take and the best assurance to give to the public. Any short-term frustration, I believe, will be repaid.

We must hold on to the independent review body for nurses' pay while it continues on the path of recognising the special needs of nurses. It is the best system we have had and there is nothing better on the horizon under any political party. Nor should we give it away for broad promises of justice for all. Those promises have failed to come to fruition before and nurses have tended to find themselves at the 'bottom of the pile'.

So where will the power of nursing come from and how will it manifest itself? I believe that if we are in step with society's values, are organised to speak with one voice and with unity then the power we have at our disposal is democratic power.

We live in a democratic society in which all governments must finally look at the public balance sheet. Nursing represents 5 per cent of the working population of the UK. Almost one in three families contains one person involved in nursing. Nursing is one of the great professions on which society depends and which it has an interest in seeing developed. In every corner of the country, in every parliamentary constituency, nurses are living or working. Hospitals now represent the largest workplaces in a majority of parliamentary constituencies in the country. In the RCN alone we have over 250,000 members working in the largest single workforce in western Europe, the NHS. They represent the largest single profession for women in the UK.

If those nurses became involved in and participate in political decision making through their nursing organisations and in their political parties I believe they will be an unstoppable force for change. We now have the organisation and are developing the public campaigning techniques to promote our ideas and arguments to the whole public. I believe this is the road down which we must go.

Participation in the political life of the country is the alternative for individual nurses to the silent frustration of the past or industrial action. I hope that other nurses will, like me, see political participation as clean and positive and not dirty and negative. Each day we spend working with people we see their needs and the services they deserve. We must look beyond the immediate frustration of not being able to give all that we would wish for today's patients but resolve as individuals, as I believe is our duty, to do everything reasonable within our power and through our nursing organisations to make sure that tomorrow's people get the nurses and the nursing they deserve. I am confident that together we can be a powerhouse for change.

Appendix I   A manifesto for nursing and health

The RCN published its manifesto for Nursing and Health in September 1986 in time for the party conference round. Its impact exceeded all expectations and it has been reprinted twice.

This appendix summarises the main points. The full version is available from the Press and Public Relations Department, Royal College of Nursing, 20 Cavendish Square, London W1A 0AP.

The Royal College of Nursing believes that to address the health needs of the 1990s, all the political parties must address the issues facing nursing. To ignore nursing questions is to ignore the realities of health care provision today and to deny the opportunities for improvement tomorrow.

1. COMMITMENT TO THE NHS

The RCN wants to see in every manifesto a commitment to the primary position of the NHS in the provision of health in this country.

2. NURSING MANPOWER

We want to see:-

a The reform of nurse education in order to cut the wastage in nurse training and to provide the nursing student with a qualification that is valid in other areas of employment.

b A programme of 'back to nursing' courses to tap the pool of qualified nurses not working in nursing.

c The introduction of more flexible working practices for women with families.
d The provision of childcare facilities for children of both pre-school and school age on health service premises.
e An increase in the numbers of men in nursing.
f Contact schemes established for those who have left the profession to have families.

---

3. NURSING EDUCATION

We want to see:-

a The end of student nurses as health authority employees.
b Nurse education as a part of higher education.
c Nurse education including more preparation for working in the community in the 1990s.
d The recognition of the rights of individual nursing students to a broader education.
e The end to the gross abuse of student nurses in the NHS.

---

4. NURSES' PAY

We want to see:-

a A complete review of the grading structure to provide a clinical career structure.
b An attack on low pay amongst the majority of nurses on the wards.
c The maintenance of the independence of the Review Body for nurses' pay and the implementation of its recommendations in full.

---

5. EXTENDING THE NURSING ROLE

We want to see:-

a The introduction of the nurse practitioner in the United Kingdom.
b Nurses given limited rights to prescribe.
c Community nursing organised into smaller neighbourhood units bringing the nurses closer to the people they serve and to the GPs they work with.
d Nursing teams given more scope on screening programmes, on

family planning advice and mental health counselling and working in the community to reach people the current service fails to reach.

6. THE STRUCTURE OF NURSING

We want to see:-

a The pay and career structure changed to provide incentives for nurses to remain in clinical work with patients.

b A clinical career structure which will reward those who enter specialist clinical areas.

c The philosophy of caring being asserted in the midst of high technology, high pressure, high turnover and acute medical care.

d Nurses who go into management retaining a clear involvement in clinical work with patients.

e A national programme for nursing research established to provide for work into the organisation of nursing and standards of care.

7. NURSES AS WOMEN

90 per cent of nurses are women. The above reforms would dramatically improve their position in work and their opportunities to go forward and fulfill their potential. The Government's failure to tackle the needs of women in nursing has resulted in both a massive waste of trained talent to the NHS and, also, in lost opportunities for the individual nurse.

THIS IS A MANIFESTO FOR ACTION

FOR NURSING

AND FOR HEALTH

Appendix II Chronology of reports and events since 1945

1945 Election of Labour government
1946 National Health Service Act
1947 Wood report on nursing education
1948 Establishment of NHS
1949 Horder report (RCN) Reconstruction Committee
1951 Election of Conservative government
1955 Re-election of Conservative government
1959 Re-election of Conservative government
1962 Hospital plan for new buildings
1964 Platt report on nursing education (RCN)
      Election of Labour government
1966 Salmon report on nursing management
      Re-election of Labour government
1968 Prices and Incomes Board report on nursing
1969 Mayston report on nursing in local government
1970 Election of Conservative government
1972 Briggs Committee on nursing education
1974 Re-organisation of NHS
      Election of Labour government (Feb)
      Halsbury report on nurses pay
      Re-election of Labour government
1976 RAWP—resources allocation
1978 Establishment of Royal Commission on NHS
1979 Jay report on mental handicap
      Nurses, Midwives and Health Visitors Act

Election of Conservative government
Patients First
Report of Royal Commission on NHS
Report of Clegg Commission on nurses pay
1983   Establishment of Pay Review Body for nurses pay
Re-election of Conservative government
Griffiths report on NHS management
1984   UKCC Code of Professional Conduct
1985   Judge report on nursing education (RCN)
1986   UKCC Project 2000 report on nurse education
Green paper on primary health care
Cumberlege report on community nursing

Appendix III Reports ready reckoner

The history of nursing since the Second World War is studded with reports and inquiries. But as Florence Nightingale put it, 'Reports are not self-executive'. Only a few were properly and effectively implemented but the names live on and can be confusing.

Because the pages of this book are liberally scattered with such references, included here is a busy person's guide to some relevant reports.

Education

Horder: Nursing Reconstruction Committee

This was set up by RCN in 1941 to examine the Athlone report and look at present needs. Produced 4 reports:

    1942 Assistant nurse
    1943 Education and training
    1943 Recruitment
    1949 Social and economic conditions

Wood: Working Party on the Recruitment and Training of Nurses

This was set up by Ministry of Health under Sir Robert Wood in 1946 and reported in 1947. The working party examined the position of the nursing profession and recommended radical educational reforms.

Platt: A Reform of Nursing Education

Set up by the RCN in 1961 and reported in 1964. Recommended the separation of education and service with a two year educational course followed by a year of controlled supervision.

Briggs: Report of the Committee on Nursing

This was set up by Secretary of State in 1970 and reported in 1972. The Committee reviewed the nurses' role and educational requirements, and proposed an 18 month course leading to the certificate in Nursing Practice followed by a further 18 months leading to registration.

Judge: The Education of Nurses—A new dispensation

This was set up by the RCN to examine the future of nurse education. It proposed the wholesale move into higher education and the separation of education and service.

Project 2000: A New Preparation for Practice

This was set up by the UKCC and reported in May 1986. It proposed the end of enrolled nurse training, a common foundation programme, five branches for specialisation and supernumerary status.

Pay

Prices and Incomes Board: Pay of Nurses and Midwives in the NHS.

This Board reported in 1968 and made recommendations covering pay, management organisation and education.

Halsbury: Committee of Inquiry into the Pay and Related Conditions of Service.

This was set up by Secretary of State and reported in 1974, recommending pay rises of up to 58 per cent.

Clegg: Standing Commission on Pay Comparability 1979

This was one of several occupational groups referred to the Commission. They recommended a raise in pay up to 25 per cent.

Pay Review Body: For Nursing Staff, Midwives, Health Visitors and Professions Allied to Medicine.

Established by the Prime Minister and first reported in 1984.

Nursing Organisation

Nuffield: The Work of Nurses in Hospital Wards

Published in 1953, this report published detailed analysis of nurses' work to examine the 'proper task' of the nurse.

The Pattern of the In-patient's Day

This was set up by the Standing Nursing Advisory Committee and reported in 1961. It recommended interalia that early waking should cease.

Salmon: Senior Nursing Staff Structure

This was set up by the Ministry of Health and reported in 1966 recommending a career structure for nurse managers. It was implemented hurriedly and rigidly.

Mayston: Management Structure in Local Authority Nursing Services

Reporting in 1969, this was similar to the Salmon report but considering the community context.

Other Relevant Reports

1974 NHS Reorganisation

This unified hospital and community services under regional and area health authorities. It introduced community health councils and gave nurses a place in teams of officers at each level.

1976 RAWP: Sharing Resources for Health in England

This proposed a system of giving fairer distribution of resources across the regional health authorities and down to areas and districts. Ten years on its progress is still slow and its effects on losing regions has been serious.

The Royal Commission on the National Health Service

Under Sir Alec Merrison, the Royal Commission reported in 1979 with the brief to consider the best use and management of the financial and manpower resources of NHS. Wide ranging conclusions were reached, but little directly involving nursing.

Jay: Committee of Inquiry into Mental Handicap Nursing and Care

Reporting in 1979, it considered the Briggs recommendation for a 'new caring profession'. It proposed a new training for staff caring for the mentally handicapped, which was then rejected but which has subsequently crept in.

Patients First 1979

This government green paper lead to the further reorganisation which abolished AHAs and preached maximum delegation.

Griffiths: NHS Management Inquiry

This was set up by the Secretary of State and reported in 1983, proposing the introduction of general managers throughout the NHS and new supervisory and management boards at the DHSS. It led to devastating effects on nurse managers.

Green Paper on Primary Health Care and the Cumberlege Report

Published together in 1986, the first largely concentrated on medical services, the second on community nursing. It proposed neighbourhood nursing schemes, limited prescribing for nurses and nurse practitioners.

Index